WAVE OPTICS
INTERFERENCE AND DIFFRACTION

By the same Author:

GEOMETRICAL OPTICS

WAVE OPTICS
Interference and Diffraction

by

C. CURRY
B.Sc., Ph.D., A.Inst.P.
Lecturer in Physics,
University of Leeds

LONDON
EDWARD ARNOLD (PUBLISHERS) LTD

Printed in Great Britain by
Richard Clay and Company, Ltd., Bungay, Suffolk

PREFACE

THE level of treatment of Interference and Diffraction in this volume lies intermediate between the elementary and more advanced accounts already available to Physics students. The aim has been to produce a book suitable for the first and second post-intermediate years of a General course, or for the first year of a three-year Special Physics course.

The author has long felt the simpler treatments available to be inadequate, while the fuller and more advanced books are somewhat heavy for a student to tackle in the early stages. A fairly comprehensive account of the subject, lucid and not too mathematical, has therefore been attempted; emphasis is placed on principles, illustrated by some representative experimental effects, and on practical applications. It is hoped that students new to the subject may find here a useful introduction, and at the same time obtain a general view of this branch of physics, unobscured by too many details and sufficient in itself for many purposes, yet supplying also an adequate basis for intelligent entrance into more advanced reading where this is necessary.

The writing of the book has strengthened the author's view that a reasonable grounding in elementary principles of geometrical optics is a desirable, if not absolutely essential, preliminary to a successful study of wave optics. Examination of the text will reveal that frequent appeal has been made by the way to matters which are sufficiently and most directly clear from simple considerations of geometrical optics. In teaching the subject this procedure is so usual that it is often done almost unconsciously, and the need for special treatment at these points (unless the students concerned are adequately informed on simple geometrical optics) requires emphasis. Where points of geometrical optics are referred to here, this is done in a manner consistent with the treatment given in the author's " Geometrical Optics ".

The composition of this book is the ultimate result of accumulation, over years, of information and ideas from various sources, and it is not easy to be aware of every source which should be acknowledged. The author is consciously indebted in some degree to each of the books listed in the bibliography, and hopes that in making acknowledgments in this way, no other volume which should receive recognition is omitted unawares.

I wish to express my thanks to the number of colleagues and others who showed interest as the writing of this book proceeded, and who gave assistance in various ways.   I am particularly grateful to Professor E. C. Stoner, F.R.S., Professor J. G. Wilson, and Mr. F. A. Long, all of whom gave a considerable amount of their time to reading the manuscript;   their helpful suggestions and general advice have been invaluable.

C. CURRY

Physics Department,
The University,
Leeds.   1956.

CONTENTS

INTRODUCTION AND PRELIMINARIES

Wave optics and geometrical optics

THE recognition of the wave nature and mode of propagation of light permits a more fundamental approach to the explanation of optical effects than is possible using only the more limited assumptions of geometrical optics. The rectilinear propagation of light in a uniform medium, which is the sole basis of the geometrical approach to optical systems, is, from the standpoint of wave optics, only an approximation; an approximation which nevertheless is sufficiently closely true in the circumstances of use of many optical instruments. The description of the behaviour of such instruments in terms of "rays" of light is therefore in many respects quite adequate. The introduction of the concept of light waves leads in such cases to results which include and agree with those arrived at by geometrical methods, but some important details and refinements in the understanding of the effects occurring are added when this more comprehensive approach is used.

Another class of optical effects is, however, entirely beyond the range of description by simple geometrical methods. This includes such phenomena as interference, diffraction, polarization, and dispersion of light; and the assumption that light is propagated in waves is essential to any explanation of these matters. Interference and diffraction of light become apparent in more special circumstances than those for which the geometrical methods are valid, and the most familiar forms of these phenomena are those characteristic of the shapes and sizes of apertures through which light beams are allowed to pass. Essentially similar effects are manifested by all types of waves, e.g., by sound waves, waves on the surface of water, as well as by light waves. Optical polarization and dispersion effects, on the other hand, depend for their explanation on the particular character of light waves. The details of the observed phenomena of this kind are only satisfactorily accounted for on the assumption that light waves are transverse and electromagnetic in nature.

Discussion of the methods used and the results obtained, at least for a representative selection of the many experiments on optical effects of this kind, and of the manner in which the wave theory is able to explain such observations and the extent to which it does so satisfactorily, must necessarily occupy a portion of any account of wave optics. A further important section must be devoted to description of practical applications based on these effects, including the principles

1

and uses of instruments such as interferometers, gratings, and polari-
meters.   Detailed aspects of the action of ordinary optical instruments,
such as microscopes and telescopes, and some important developments
of these instruments suggested by wave-optical considerations, also
belong essentially to this subject.

The present volume deals with the phenomena of interference and
diffraction of light in these various connections.   A representative
selection of material is made, with the object of elucidating basic
principles, and the kinds of practical applications of the effects are
discussed.

Outline of history of wave optics

The sequence of discoveries of relevant facts and of developments
in understanding of any branch of physical science is almost always a
somewhat disorderly one.   This is certainly true of wave optics, and
arrangement of the topics concerned in a different order from that in
which they were first investigated is desirable in a logically connected
development of the principles of the subject and its applications.   It
is convenient to present here a brief outline of the history of wave
optics, which, when read in conjunction with what follows, should
permit the subject to be seen in its historical perspective, and at the
same time allow freedom from a great amount of historical digression
when the physics of the subject is under discussion.

The history of the development of wave optics opens with a small
group of experimental observations made during the latter half of the
seventeenth century.   Several wave-optical phenomena of diverse
kinds were then discovered, and, since the effects were in most cases
merely observed without any satisfactory explanation being possible,
their interconnection was not clearly evident at the time.   The principal names associated with this early period are those of Grimaldi,
Hooke, Bartholinus, Huygens, and Newton.   During the following
century observations of a similar character were reported by various
workers, but no marked advance in the explanation of the observed
phenomena was made.   A really satisfactory understanding, on wave-
optical principles, of the various observed effects began to be developed
soon after the commencement of the nineteenth century.   This second
major period of advance opened with the vital work of Young and
Fresnel; and, along with these, several other investigators of the
nineteenth century must be mentioned as having made contributions of
special value towards a rapidly deepening understanding of the fundamentals of the subject.

Reference will be made in turn to important contributions made by
prominent investigators until towards the close of the nineteenth
century, when a basic understanding of wave optics (especially of

interference and diffraction) may be said to have been well established. Detailed developments, since this time, of theoretical and experimental aspects of interference and diffraction are too numerous and complex for inclusion in a brief outline.

Grimaldi studied intensity variations near the edges of shadows of obstacles. Objects such as fine hairs, rectangular corners of opaque bodies, etc., were used to cast the shadows, and the intensity patterns were essentially Fresnel diffraction patterns; some of these were complex, since the objects were not always of a simple kind. The work was published in 1665, two years after Grimaldi's death. **Hooke** reported observations of a similar nature in 1672, and also performed some experiments on white-light fringes with thin films. Meanwhile (1669) **Bartholinus** discovered the property of a calcite crystal of forming a double image when a single object is viewed through it. The phenomenon of double refraction, discovered in this way, awaited the concept of transverse light waves and the polarization of light for its explanation.

Huygens performed experiments of a more systematic kind on double refraction; his best-known contribution to wave optics is, however, his explanation of rectilinear propagation assuming the wave nature of light. He used his principle of secondary waves to account for reflection and refraction phenomena, and also extended this to a partial explanation of double refraction, assuming ellipsoidal forms for the extraordinary wave-fronts. He also had some understanding that transverse waves were a necessary supposition for the explanation of this phenomenon. His " Traité de la Lumière " was published in 1678.

In the field of optics **Newton's** best-known work is perhaps that on dispersion and the composition of white light. His advocacy of the corpuscular theory of light, and his controversy with Huygens, are also well known. All the elementary wave-optical effects had at that time been observed, Newton's rings being a further example of effects of the interference type then known. Attempts at explanation of these effects in terms of the corpuscular theory * were made by Newton ; none of these explanations was satisfactory, but most of the observations were not then accounted for on the basis of the wave nature of light, and the wave theory seemed untenable to Newton because of the known non-rectilinear effects obtained with other kinds of waves. Newton's " Opticks " appeared in 1704, and the corpuscular theory remained in the ascendancy during the ensuing century. The high respect accorded to Newton's views was partly responsible for this.

* In attempting to explain diffraction and interference effects, Newton introduced into his theory a vibrating ether affecting the movements of the corpuscles The theory was not, therefore, a purely corpuscular one.

Though the implications of their results were by no means immediately accepted, the revival of the wave theory is mostly attributable to the researches in optics performed by **Young** (1801–4) and by **Fresnel** (1815–26). Young conceived the idea of interference of waves as a result of study of acoustical effects in the first place. He was able ultimately to produce similar effects with light, though on a very different scale, the best known of which is the double-slit interference experiment. The corpuscular theory had no real explanation for these results, whereas their explanation on the principle of superposition, introduced by Young, was fairly clear. This revival of the wave theory of light propagation met with considerable resistance at first, and it was only becoming well established after a considerable amount of work had also been performed by Fresnel. Fresnel, without knowledge of Young's earlier work, used the principle of superposition in explanation of his observations on diffraction and really laid the essential basis of diffraction theory. He realized that this principle of superposition could be applied to all the waves from the extended distribution of secondary sources, which, according to Huygens' principle, constitute the wavefront passed by any aperture. Explanations of diffraction patterns formed by a large variety of apertures and obstacles were immediately possible, and the correspondence between prediction and experiment confirmed in many cases. At the same time the basis of Huygens' construction of advancing wave-fronts became clearer, unrestricted wave-fronts only producing strictly rectilinear propagation, and diffraction effects arising because of the apertures through which the waves necessarily have to pass. Though certain assumptions introduced by Fresnel awaited later justification by more comprehensive theories of diffraction (by **Stokes, Kirchhoff,** and others), use of the ideas introduced by Fresnel remains adequate for the prediction and general understanding of most simple diffraction effects.

The discovery by **Malus** (in 1808) of the polarization by reflection of light at an appropriate angle of incidence upon a glass plate (and the possibility of using two glass plates in this way as polarizer and analyser) provided vital information leading to understanding of the nature of light waves. After some time, and despite opposition to his view, Fresnel gradually realized that this effect found its true explanation in the fact that transverse waves were involved in the propagation of light. He developed the *elastic solid theory*, in which the waves were imagined as transverse vibrations in the *ether*, which was considered as an all-pervading elastic material. The Fresnel equations (which explain relative transmitted and reflected light amplitudes at interfaces between optical media) were deduced in this way; much later they were shown to be obtainable from the electromagnetic theory of light, in a manner which was more satisfactory in some details.

The understanding of interference and diffraction effects, gained in this period, made possible determinations of light wavelengths. **Fraunhofer** (around 1821), besides making diffraction observations, developed grating production methods and spectroscopic techniques, which, along with his discovery of the absorption lines in the solar spectrum, made possible more accurate measurements on dispersive properties of materials.

The advances in the understanding of electrical and magnetic phenomena associated with such names as **Oersted, Ampère, Faraday** and **Henry,** etc., were also taking place more or less simultaneously. The understanding of these effects, together with confirmatory evidence provided by the discovery of the **Faraday** magneto-optical effect (1845) and the **Kerr** electro-optical effect (1865), provided the basis of the electromagnetic theory of light, introduced by **Maxwell** (1864). Velocity of light measurements by **Fizeau** (1849) and **Foucault** (1850), of higher accuracy than the earlier determinations by **Römer** (1676) and **Bradley** (1727), provided supporting evidence. The possibility of obtaining the velocity of light in various media (e.g., in water, as well as in air and *in vacuo*) arose along with the development of these terrestrial methods ; and the relative velocities in different media gave support to the wave mode of propagation. The velocity expected from Maxwell's theory was confirmed, especially by the more accurate determinations, first in air and later *in vacuo*, made by methods later developed by **Michelson.** The artificial production of electromagnetic radiation, by **Hertz,** and the confirmation that its velocity was the same as that of light, and thus in agreement also with the predictions of the theory, came twenty-three years after the actual theory.

The work of **Cauchy** (1836) and **Sellmeier** (1871), which opened the development of dispersion theory, also belongs to the period under survey. Really rapid development in the understanding of matters such as absorption and dispersion came only after the establishment of the electromagnetic theory.

This outline of the early history of wave optics emphasizes salient points only. Many important contributions of a more detailed nature are necessarily passed over. The names of **Brewster, Babinet,** and **Cornu** may perhaps be specially mentioned in this connection. Some of these contributions, as well as much recent work in the fields of interference and diffraction, are described more appropriately in the main text.

CHAPTER 1

WAVE MOTION AND SUPERPOSITION OF WAVES

SOME of the simpler concepts of wave motion, including the meanings of some basic terms, are discussed first in this chapter. Secondly, a brief introduction is given to the kind of considerations which appear repeatedly in the remainder of the book, i.e., the effects of compounding two or more wave systems, and the kinds of mathematical methods of describing such effects. Attention is confined to harmonic waves, i.e., waves of simple sinusoidal form.

Wave Motion

Consider a wave of sinusoidal form travelling along the x axis. The displacement curve at a particular instant of time may be represented by the expression

$$y = a \sin (qx + \phi)$$

where a, q, and ϕ are constants. y passes through a cycle of values for each increment of 2π in qx, so that the wave form repeats itself at

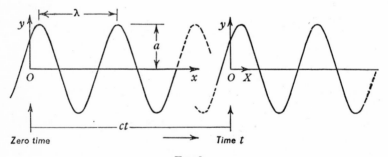

Zero time   Time t

FIG. 1A.

regular distances of $2\pi/q$ along the x axis. The extreme values of y are $+a$ and $-a$. The distance $2\pi/q$ is known as the *wavelength* λ, and a is termed the *amplitude* of the wave considered. The form of the curve is shown in Fig. 1A. If the whole wave form advances with velocity c along the positive direction of x, the effect may be represented by supposing the origin O to move a distance ct in time t, when the form of the wave expressed in terms of the new abscissa X will be

6

unchanged. The new X is clearly $(x - ct)$; hence the equation representing the advancing wave is

$$y = a \sin \left[q(x - ct) + \phi \right] = a \sin \left[\frac{2\pi}{\lambda} (x - ct) + \phi \right]$$

A sinusoidal wave advances in this way by simple harmonic motion (in the transverse direction) of every point in the wave profile, the *time period* T of this motion being also the time in which the wave profile moves forward a distance equal to one wavelength. The *frequency* ν of the wave motion is the number of oscillations per unit time. The reciprocal k of the wavelength, or number of wavelengths in unit distance, is termed the *wave number*. These quantities are clearly related in the following way :

$$c = \frac{\lambda}{T} = \nu\lambda = \frac{\nu}{k}$$

The quantity $\left[\dfrac{2\pi}{\lambda} (x - ct) + \phi \right]$ is known as the phase angle, and more often simply as the *phase* of the motion. Alternative expressions for the phase, making use of the other quantities defined above are :

$$\left[2\pi \left(\frac{x}{\lambda} - \frac{t}{T} \right) + \phi \right], \left[2\pi \left(\frac{x}{\lambda} - \nu t \right) + \phi \right], \left[2\pi(kx - \nu t) + \phi \right]$$

For sinusoidal waves of constant frequency, travelling at constant velocity, the phase of the motion depends on :

(*a*) The position in the wave system concerned, i.e., on x, increasing regularly with distance in the direction of motion; the above expressions for the phase angle make it clear that points λ apart in the wave system differ in phase by 2π.

(*b*) The time, t; at any point in the wave system the phase angle decreases uniformly with time, changing by 2π in every interval of time T, i.e., as a length λ of the wave form passes the point concerned.

(*c*) The value of ϕ, which is the initial phase when t and x are zero, and is termed the *phase constant* or *epoch* of the motion. Two waves which differ only in ϕ, by an amount $\Delta\phi$, are relatively displaced in the x direction by an amount which depends on $\Delta\phi$. The x displacement corresponding to the angle $\Delta\phi$ is $\dfrac{\Delta\phi}{2\pi} . \lambda$.

It should be realized that, in order to display the forms of the waves effectively, the curves drawn must necessarily be transverse to the direction in which the waves advance, but this does not in any way limit the discussion to waves of a transverse nature. It is equally applicable to scalar quantities, the magnitudes of which at points along any line may be represented graphically by displacements perpendicular to that line. With sound waves, for instance, the pressure in the medium conveying the sound varies with time and position, and is a scalar quantity. With light waves the varying quantities are electric and magnetic intensities; these are vectors and are directed perpendicular to the direction of propagation; but this fact is not essential to the understanding of interference and diffraction phenomena. It has been sufficient so far to discuss waves of constant amplitude; though a is not usually a constant quantity, more often decreasing with increase of x, for example. The quantities defined are of the same significance when a is not constant.

Superposition of waves

Interference and diffraction effects occur generally when several wave systems are being propagated at the same time through some

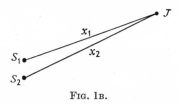

FIG. 1B.

region; and the basic principles of explanation of these effects may be made clear by reference to a simple, and in some respects hypothetical, case. This is illustrated in Fig. 1B, which shows two sources S_1 and S_2, which are imagined for the present as having infinitesimally small dimensions. The sources are considered to be similar, i.e., each emitting light waves of the same amplitude and wavelength; and the surrounding medium is uniform so that the velocity of light is constant everywhere in the region. Let J be a general point, distant x_1 from S_1 and x_2 from S_2. The phase of the wave through J from S_1 at time t is $\left[\dfrac{2\pi}{\lambda}(x_1 - ct) + \phi_1\right]$, where ϕ_1 is the phase constant for the source S_1. A similar expression may be written for the phase of the wave from S_2 at the same time. The *phase difference* δ between the waves at J is thus

$$\delta = \left[\frac{2\pi}{\lambda}(x_2 - x_1) + (\phi_2 - \phi_1)\right] \quad . \quad . \quad . \quad \textbf{1.1}$$

Each of the phases decreases uniformly with time, but the difference δ between them is seen to remain constant provided $(\phi_2 - \phi_1)$ is invariant with time.

The magnitude of the phase difference δ depends on $(\phi_2 - \phi_1)$, i.e., the difference in phase between the waves as they are emitted from the sources; and also on $(x_2 - x_1)$, the geometrical difference in the lengths of the paths to the point J traversed by the two wave systems. δ varies with the position of the point J, because of the changing magnitude of $(x_2 - x_1)$ from point to point.

The phase difference δ may, if desired, be written

$$\delta = \frac{2\pi}{\lambda}\left[(x_2 - x_1) + \frac{\lambda}{2\pi} (\phi_2 - \phi_1) \right]$$

Thus $\frac{\lambda}{2\pi}(\phi_2 - \phi_1)$ may be considered as that addition to the geometrical path difference necessary to give the path difference equivalent to the whole difference of phase at the point J. This equivalent path difference is termed the *optical path difference*, and is identical with the geometrical path difference when $(\phi_2 - \phi_1) = 0$.

It is next necessary to consider the effect at the point J of the addition of two harmonic motions having the constant phase difference δ. Any simple harmonic motion of amplitude a may be considered as the projection on the diameter of a circle of a point moving round its circumference with uniform speed, the radius of the circle being a. This is illustrated in Fig. 1c. As the radius OA rotates with angular velocity ω, the foot B of the perpendicular from A upon the vertical diameter moves with simple harmonic motion. If OA makes an initial angle ψ with the horizontal, then the angle after time t is $(\psi - \omega t)$ if the rotation is clockwise, and

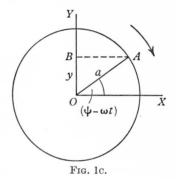

Fig. 1c.

$$y = a \sin (\psi - \omega t)$$

ψ is the initial phase of the motion, and T the periodic time is $2\pi/\omega$. Clockwise rotation of the radius OA has been specified so that the phase of the motion decreases uniformly with time; this, as has been seen previously, occurs at any point (such as J in Fig. 1b) through which a harmonic wave is passing with constant velocity.

When a point is subject to two such motions, of the same time period but with a constant phase difference δ, the separate displacements of the point in each of the motions add together to give the total displacement at any time. Fig. 1d shows two diagrams, each similar to Fig. 1c, superposed; y_1 and y_2 are the two displacements. The difference between the angles A_2OX and A_1OX, which are respectively $(\psi_2 - \omega t)$ and $(\psi_1 - \omega t)$, remains constant as OA_1 and OA_2 sweep round the figure. It is clear that the sum y of the displacements y_1 and y_2 is OB, the projection on OY of the diagonal OA of the parallelogram which has OA_1 and OA_2 as its sides. The point B executes simple harmonic motion about O as OA rotates in its position intermediate between OA_1 and OA_2. The phase of the resultant motion clearly bears a constant relation to

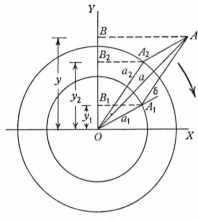

FIG. 1D.

that of either of its components, determined by the trigonometry of the triangle OA_1A. More important is the relation between the amplitudes of the resultant motion and of its components.

From triangle OA_1A

$$a^2 = a_1{}^2 + a_2{}^2 + 2a_1a_2 \cos \delta \quad . \quad . \quad . \quad . \quad \textbf{1.2}$$

When δ is zero, or an even multiple of π

$$a = a_1 + a_2$$

but when δ is an odd multiple of π

$$a = a_1 \sim a_2$$

In these two respective cases the separate amplitudes simply add or subtract numerically, and the motions are commonly said to be *in phase* or *out of phase*. More generally, the resultant amplitude lies between the extreme values $(a_1 + a_2)$ and $(a_1 - a_2)$.

Returning to the example illustrated in Fig. 1B, it is now clear that the resultant amplitudes of the combined wave systems will differ according to the situation of J. In the simpler cases of interference and diffraction, distances such as x_1 and x_2 are large in comparison with

S_1S_2 and with λ, in the circumstances of observation of the effects. This means that x_1 and x_2 are closely equal in both magnitude and direction; and it will appear later that these two factors determine the amplitudes at J. Thus, it is possible at a point J sufficiently distant from S_1 and S_2, to treat the separate amplitudes in the two wave systems as being equal. The resultant amplitude is thus zero where the waves are out of phase. Where they are in phase the amplitude of the combined wave system is double that contributed by either wave separately.

When $a_1 = a_2$ the expression 1.2 becomes

$$a^2 = 2a_1^2(1 + \cos \delta)$$

or
$$a = 2a_1 \cos \frac{\delta}{2} \quad . \quad . \quad . \quad . \quad . \quad 1.3$$

The variations of a and of a^2 with δ are shown in Fig. 1E (i) and (ii). It may be shown that the energy of the motion depends on the square of the amplitude, i.e., is proportional to a_1^2 in each separate wave system

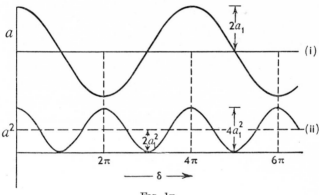

FIG. 1E.

at all points such as J (Fig. 1B) where the amplitudes due to S_1 or S_2 have the value a_1. Curve (ii) of Fig. 1E shows that the average value of the square of the resultant amplitude is $2a_1^2$, i.e., that the average energy at points such as J is, as might be expected, the sum of the energies in the separate waves; the actual energy does, however, vary considerably from point to point. At some of these points it is four times that in one of the wave systems alone; while at others it is zero, complete cancellation of the wave systems occurring at these places. The term *interference* of the waves applies most appropriately at these latter positions, but is used also in a more general way implying changes in the energy distribution brought about by superposition of one wave system upon another as they pass through some common region of their path.

The equation 1.1 gives the magnitude of the phase difference at the point J in terms of the distances of J from the two sources

$$\delta = \left[\frac{2\pi}{\lambda}(x_2 - x_1) + (\phi_2 - \phi_1)\right] \quad . \quad . \quad . \quad 1.1$$

It is clear that δ has the same constant value for all points such that $(x_2 - x_1)$ is constant. In any plane through S_1 and S_2 such points lie on a hyperbola having S_1 and S_2 as its foci. Several such hyperbolæ, corresponding to $(x_2 - x_1)$ values of 0, $\pm\lambda$, $\pm2\lambda$, etc., are shown in Fig. 1F. The parts of the curves to the right of the line S_1S_2 only are shown, though they may be continued similarly to the left. In three

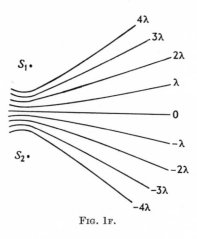

FIG. 1F.

dimensions the surfaces of constant δ are hyperboloids, obtained by rotating these hyperbolæ about S_1S_2.

If $(\phi_2 - \phi_1) = 0$, i.e., if the waves emitted from S_1 and S_2 are in phase, these particular curves correspond to δ values of 0, $\pm2\pi$, $\pm4\pi$, etc., i.e., they are the loci of points where maximum reinforcement of the two wave systems occurs. Generally where the optical path difference is $m\lambda$ or the phase difference $2m\pi$, where m is an integer, the *mth order* of reinforcement of the wave systems is said to occur. At distances from S_1 and S_2 which are large compared with S_1S_2 the hyperbolæ of Fig. 1F approximate very closely to their asymptotes; these are straight lines all intersecting at the mid-point of S_1S_2.

If $(\phi_2 - \phi_1) \neq 0$, i.e., if there is a difference in phase between the waves emitted from the sources, the hyperbolæ drawn in Fig. 1F do not necessarily correspond to the maxima in the resultant amplitude of the wave system. It is evident from equation 1.1 that the hyperbolæ

$$(x_2 - x_1) = 0, \lambda, 2\lambda \ldots \text{ etc.}$$

are the loci of points having respective δ values of

$$\delta = [\phi_2 - \phi_1], [2\pi + (\phi_2 - \phi_1)], [4\pi + (\phi_2 - \phi_1)] \ldots \text{ etc.}$$

Thus the series of a^2 values in Fig. 1E (ii) at points $(\phi_2 - \phi_1)$ to the right of each of the successive maxima, is appropriate to the series of hyperbolæ shown in Fig. 1F.

A special case of some interest is that in which $(\phi_2 - \phi_1) = \pi$, i.e., the waves are exactly out of phase as they are emitted from S_1 and S_2. The δ values appropriate to the hyperbolæ of Fig. 1F are then $\pi, 3\pi, 5\pi$, etc., and these hyperbolæ then correspond to loci of points where the waves cancel. The phase difference of π on emission is equivalent to a contribution of $\lambda/2$ to the optical path, and as a result the waves cancel in exactly those positions where maximum reinforcement would occur if there were no phase difference at the sources.

It should be noted that, whatever the value of $(\phi_2 - \phi_1)$, the distribution around the sources of the resultant amplitudes remains stationary with time provided $(\phi_2 - \phi_1)$ remains constant. In addition to having sources of the same wavelength and amplitude, it is therefore essential that a constant phase relationship between the emissions from the sources must be maintained continuously if such effects are to be observed. Sources of this kind are termed *coherent sources*. It is a feature of all light sources that discontinuities in the phase of emission occur intermittently at very short intervals.*

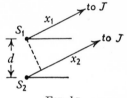

Fig. 1G.

To obtain coherent sources it is therefore necessary to use one single source in order to provide two (or more) effective sources, so that these discontinuities occur in both sources in the same way and at the same time, thus ensuring that the difference in their phases is invariant with time.

The two sources S_1 and S_2 of Fig. 1B are drawn on a larger scale in Fig. 1G, and the point J is considered at a distance large compared with S_1S_2, so that the directions to it from S_1 and S_2 may be considered

---

* This is connected with the finite spectral breadth of emissions from light sources, and the intermittent emission of wave groups rather than continuous emission of infinite wave trains (see p. 16). A *limiting path difference* for interference is set by the fact that the groups emitted by even the finest spectral lines are of limited length. For this reason experiments using large path difference (see p. 122) require very careful selection and control of the source to be used.

parallel. This is equivalent to the assumption that J is sufficiently distant that the hyperbola on which it lies (see Fig. 1F) may be considered coincident with its asymptote. Let θ be the angle made by the direction to J (from S_1 or S_2) with the normal to S_1S_2; and let $S_1S_2 = d$. Then the geometrical path difference

$$(x_2 - x_1) = d \sin \theta$$

Assuming the simple case in which $\phi_1 = \phi_2$

$$\delta = \frac{2\pi}{\lambda} \cdot d \sin \theta$$

The maxima therefore occur along directions such that

$$\sin \theta = m \frac{\lambda}{d}$$

and the minima such that

$$\sin \theta = (m + \tfrac{1}{2}) \frac{\lambda}{d}$$

These expressions show the necessity of using small values of d if appreciable values of θ are to be obtained with light waves, since the wavelength λ is so small.

Graphical methods of compounding harmonic motions

It has been shown on p. 10 how the amplitudes of two harmonic motions add vectorially to give the amplitude of the resultant motion. For example, the motions having amplitudes a_1 and a_2 and phase difference δ superpose to give the resultant amplitude a, in the manner indicated in Fig. 1D and also in the equation 1.2. It is evident on consideration that more than two motions superpose according to similar principles, the resultant amplitude being the closing side of a polygon, the other sides of which represent by their magnitudes and directions the amplitudes and phases of the separate motions. The graphical construction of such a polygon is often a simpler means of arriving at the resultant amplitude than the alternative trigonometrical determination (exemplified in the simple case by equation 1.2), and will often be used in the ensuing pages. A drawing of this kind, representing the effect of superposing harmonic motions, is frequently termed a *phase-amplitude diagram*.

The case so far considered has been an imaginary one in some respects. The sources S_1 and S_2 were imagined of dimensions quite small compared with λ, the wavelength of the light considered. In practice there are always differences in distance to the point J (Fig. 1B) from points in the same source (e.g., S_1), so that appreciable phase differences exist between the amplitude contributions at J due to different parts of the same source. The more general problem to be considered is therefore that of summation of the amplitude contributions at some point J due to the very large number of elemental portions of the area of the source, each of which is at a slightly different distance from J.

Let PQ (Fig. 1H (i)) represent the extended area of a small source of light, all the elemental portions of this area being considered to be coherent sources. Let Δs represent that small portion of the area which is at distance x from J. The amplitudes of the contributions at J, due to all such portions, depend on the areas Δs (as well as on the distances x and the directions of these distances). Their phases at any instant

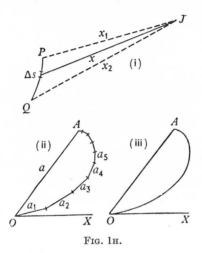

Fig. 1H.

depend on the values of x, which range between x_1 and x_2, these being the x values for the parts of the source nearest and most remote from J (say P and Q). Thus the phase-amplitude diagram is of the kind suggested by Fig. 1H (ii), a large number of small amplitude contributions a_1, a_2, a_3, . . . etc., at progressively greater inclinations to the horizontal adding together vectorially to give the resultant a, which is the closing side of the polygon. This discussion is clearly only really valid when the small areas Δs are of infinitesimal size and their number approaches infinity. The phase-amplitude diagram (Fig. 1H (iii)) then becomes a smooth curve, and the resultant amplitude a is the chord OA joining the two ends of this curve. As in the simpler case illustrated in Fig. 1D, the whole figure must be imagined rotating about O continuously, as all the phases change at the same uniform rate with time. The angle between the tangents to the curve at the points O

and A is the largest difference in phase between the contributions at J. This is clearly $\dfrac{2\pi}{\lambda}\,(x_2 - x_1)$, x_2 and x_1 being the longest and shortest distances from the area to J.

Wave groups

A consideration which must be borne in mind, to which brief reference here is sufficient, is the fact that no source actually emits light of absolutely single-valued wavelength (or frequency). The distribution

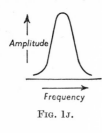

with frequency of the amplitude emitted for a single spectral line often takes the form indicated in Fig. 1J ; and while the range of frequencies may be extremely narrow, it is nevertheless always finite. An infinite train of waves of the relevant wavelength corresponds to each frequency emitted. The combination of all these waves, with due regard to their amplitude, results in a non-infinite train of waves, or *wave group*. For example, a wave train of the form suggested in Fig. 1K would correspond to the spectral line shown in Fig. 1J. Generally, the narrower the range of frequency of the constituent wave trains, the longer the wave group resulting from their combination.

FIG. 1J.

The reverse of this process is also possible, i.e., any arbitrary wave form may be considered as the sum of many infinite wave trains, the amplitudes of which are distributed continuously with frequency. Books on Fourier analysis may be consulted by the reader interested in this subject. For the understanding of the subjects dealt with in the present volume it is sufficient to realize that the earlier considerations

FIG. 1K.

of this chapter are applicable separately to all of the constituent infinite wave trains which together form the emission from any light source.

It will be seen in the next chapter that seemingly simple phenomena, such as rectilinear propagation, reflection, and refraction of light, are themselves effects of superposition of many wave systems after the manner outlined in this chapter. Later chapters are devoted to particular cases of the kinds of effects for which the terms interference and diffraction are usually reserved, making use of the fundamental concepts already defined.

CHAPTER 2

PROPAGATION, REFLECTION, AND REFRACTION OF WAVES

THE suggestion that light is propagated in waves meets the immediate difficulty that, if this is so, it is not obvious why light should travel in straight lines. Newton, at the time when the first suggestions as to the wave nature of light were making their appearance, considered this to be an insuperable objection to the theory. Huygens' major contribution to this aspect of optics was to advance arguments supporting the view that rectilinear propagation would, in certain circumstances, be the expected outcome of the wave nature of light; and to demonstrate that the effects of reflection and refraction (and double refraction) were also explicable on the basis of his understanding of the mode of propagation of light.

Huygens' principle, that optical phenomena may be accounted for by a method of construction of advancing wave-fronts (shortly to be described), was only partially understood and explained by Huygens himself, but it gives correct results, and that it has a sound basis has been shown by subsequent developments of the wave theory of light. It is known now to be correct and accurate only when no restrictions on the extent of the wave-fronts are considered. Huygens did not consider the possible consequences of imposing limitations on the wave-fronts, and was unaware of the close connection between his theory of wave propagation and the explanation of diffraction effects. The work of Fresnel, over a century later, supplied the first real clarification of the reasons for the validity of Huygens' principle in most normal circumstances, and at the same time provided the key to the understanding of diffraction effects.

The concept of wave-fronts, and how they advance according to Huygens' principle, will be discussed first in this chapter. This will be followed by a brief indication, sufficient only for the present purpose (but to be enlarged in Chapter 4), of the way in which Huygens' principle is justified in the light of Fresnel's and other developments of the underlying theory of wave propagation. This discussion will at the same time make clear the circumstances in which departures from rectilinear propagation arise. Confining attention to circumstances in which Huygens' principle adequately represents the facts (i.e., to wave-fronts of appreciable extent) it will then be shown that the laws of reflection and refraction, and all the consequent properties of mirrors, prisms, and lenses deducible by the methods of geometrical optics, may be explained by the wave theory of light.

The propagation of waves according to Huygens' principle

Imagine a source of light S (Fig. 2A) in a uniform medium in which the velocity of light is constant, and consider the effects of emission in directions within a limited solid angle, the section of which in the plane of the figure is the angle ASB. If rectilinear propagation is assumed, the light is advancing equally in all radial directions from S, and the light disturbance emitted at any instant should, at some later time, be crossing a spherical surface having S at its centre (e.g., PQ in Fig. 2A). It should, furthermore, be equally spread over this surface. A succession of such surfaces, equally spaced, may thus be considered to represent the successive positions at which the light disturbance has arrived at regular intervals after its emission. Huy-

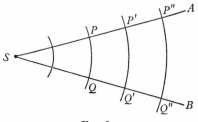

FIG. 2A.

gens' principle attempts to show, on the basis of a wave conception of light propagation, that the disturbance spread over one such surface (often called a *wave-front*) must later, of necessity, be found in a similar surface having the same form and centre of curvature as the original one (e.g., $P'Q'$). It is evident that, if this is shown to be true, rectilinear propagation is explained. Alternatively, in any circumstances for which it is no longer true, rectilinear propagation would no longer be expected.

Huygens assumed that any wave-front PQ (Fig. 2B) may be considered as a very large number of centres of disturbance, such as X, Y, and Z; which disturbances will at a later time have passed onwards to the surfaces of spheres centred on these points. The disturbances originating at points such as X, Y, and Z are termed *secondary waves*. The combined effect of all these disturbances, distributed in this way, is the wave-front at this later time. The combined effect of all the secondary waves is to produce, according to Huygens, a disturbance now lying entirely in the single surface tangential to all the secondary surfaces; for example, the surface represented by $P'Q'$ in Fig. 2B. It is clear that, since all the secondary surfaces have a constant radius at any instant after leaving PQ, the new surface $P'Q'$, constructed in this way, fulfils the requirements mentioned above, i.e., it has the same form and centre of curvature as the original surface PQ.

Since the secondary waves are of complete spherical form, *two* surfaces exist which are tangential to all the secondary waves at some instant after the disturbance lies in PQ. The second of these is of smaller radius than PQ, and corresponds to light propagation towards the source. The latter possibility for the new wave-front is simply ignored in using Huygens' construction, though no valid reason for doing this is apparent from simple considerations. Even the later Fresnel theory, which in other respects affords justification for Huygens' construction, accounts for the absence of the reverse wave in a somewhat artificial way (by introduction of the so-called inclination factor), and the justification for this awaited the appearance of more comprehensive diffraction theories.

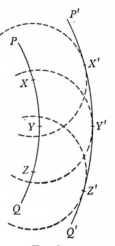

FIG. 2B.

Huygens considered that the disturbances propagated in the way described by his con-
struction were intermittent pulses of short duration, the time variation of the amplitude occupying a brief interval only as the disturbance passed any point in the region surrounding the source. No understanding of the basis of Huygens' principle is possible so long as pulse disturbances of this kind are considered. The construction really assumes that the secondary disturbances from the various elements of a wave-front, such as those arising at X, Y, and Z (Fig. 2B), which later are spread over spherical surfaces centred on these points, must nevertheless be of zero magnitude everywhere except at the small regions of those surfaces in directions perpendicularly forward from the original wave-front (i.e., near points such as X', Y', and Z'). This assumption is evidently one which begs the question. Reasons for its validity become apparent only when the idea of continuous wave trains, first suggested by Fresnel, is introduced. The disturbance at the source must be considered as periodic and sustained over appreciable intervals, so that waves of constant time period pass outward through the region surrounding the source S. It is evident that successive spherical surfaces, such as are drawn in Fig. 2A, may then be made to represent successive crests (or troughs) in the wave system, which is continually spreading outward from S.

More generally, any such surface, around a source S, emitting a disturbance varying sinusoidally with time, represents a locus of points having the same phase of motion. All such surfaces move outward from S, and their new positions are determinable by Huygens' construction, the validity of which may be shown, on these suppositions, in a more satisfactory way. The Fresnel treatment of advancing waves is indicated in the following section, and developed more fully in Chapter 4.

Circumstances of validity of Huygens' construction

Let PQ be a portion of a spherical surface having its centre at a source of light S. At any instant the disturbances at all points in such a surface are in phase. The phase of the motion in PQ at this instant will at a later time have passed on to another similar surface (e.g., $P'Q'$ in Fig. 2A), while that which was present in an earlier surface will

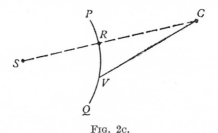

FIG. 2c.

have reached PQ. Consider now some point C, on the other side of PQ from S (Fig. 2c). The amplitude at C at any instant t may be regarded as the vector sum of the amplitudes from all parts of PQ. The contribution to this amplitude from an element of area at the point V, for instance, is a disturbance which has travelled the distance VC since leaving the surface PQ. Thus it corresponds in phase to the surface of constant phase passing through PQ at the time $\left(t - \dfrac{VC}{c}\right)$, where c is the velocity of light. The distance VC varies considerably, as V is chosen at different positions on PQ (except in one special case to be mentioned later). It is therefore clear in a simple way that phase differences must exist between the various contributions to the amplitude at C at time t. Since a phase difference of 2π is introduced by a change in VC of λ, the wavelength of light, and the latter is of very small magnitude, it follows that the contributions to the resultant amplitude at C differ in phase over a very wide range. The effects of many parts of the area PQ may therefore be expected to cancel; and the full development of these principles * leads to the result that the amplitude at C depends almost entirely upon a small area of PQ around R, the foot of the perpendicular to PQ from C. The remainder of the area PQ makes an amplitude contribution at C which is effectively zero ; and this, as will be seen in Chapter 4, remains true even if this outer area of PQ (away from R) is partially obscured by some obstacle or screen.

Consider now the points D, E, and F (Fig. 2D), in addition to the point C, and imagine some obstacle which may be inserted so as to obstruct the waves passing over the portion MQ of the surface PQ. The resultant amplitude at C will be unchanged by the insertion of this obstacle, since the small area near R which contributes to the amplitude at C is not impeded by the obstacle. The amplitude at D will be reduced to zero, however, since the area near T is completely obstructed. Illumination will thus be unaffected at points such as C, well outside

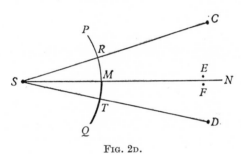

FIG. 2D.

the geometrical shadow of the obstacle ; it will also be reduced to zero at points such as D, sufficiently inside the geometrical shadow. Near the geometrical shadow edge N, more complicated effects occur. The small area near the foot of the perpendicular to the wave-front from a point like E or F is partly obscured by the edge M of the obstacle, to an extent which differs according to the point chosen ; and the resultant amplitude from the non-obscured portion varies considerably from point to point in the region of E and F. Intensity variations, known as diffraction patterns, therefore occur in the vicinity of the shadow edge. The cause of such effects is the restriction of the extent of the wave-front by the insertion of the obstacle. All beams of light used in practice are limited by the apertures of the systems through which they pass, but these apertures are normally quite large, so that wide beams are passed. It is now evident that the wave-fronts of considerable

---

* Allowing for the fact that the magnitude of the amplitude contribution at C due to V depends on VC and also on the inclination of VC to the normal at V. See discussion on the inclination factor (p. 56).

extent passed by these apertures will, over their main area, advance according to Huygens' principle, each small portion of this main area contributing effects in the directly forward direction only. Only very near the extremities of a wave-front, set by the aperture through which it passes, will departures from rectilinear propagation occur.

A particular and important case, in which the above discussion is no longer appropriate, must now be discussed separately.

Imagine a portion of a spherical wave-front PQ which, as a result of passage through some optical system, is concave towards the direction in which it is advancing (Fig. 2E). Suppose it is required to find the effect at a point C, quite near to F, the centre of curvature of the wave-front, i.e., near the point at which the wave-front focuses. As before, the contribution at C at time t due to an element at a point V on the

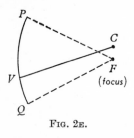

FIG. 2E.

surface PQ has the phase which is common to the whole surface PQ at time $\left(t - \dfrac{VC}{c}\right)$. In this case, since C is close to F, the distances VC are not greatly different for all the points such as V; thus the phases of the disturbances at C do not vary over a very wide range. When C is actually at F all the amplitude contributions are exactly in phase, and so simply add together to give the total amplitude. As C is moved away from F (in any direction) the phases are spread over a small range at first; and the resultant amplitude falls because of this dephasing of its components. The range of the phases depends on the range of values of VC, and this increases as C is taken farther from F; and for any position of C relative to F it clearly also depends on the angular aperture subtended at F by the wave-front PQ, increasing with this aperture. The amplitude therefore falls off away from F, more quickly the larger the aperture. At some points the vector addition of all the amplitudes may result in complete cancellation of all the waves; elsewhere generally some resultant amplitude remains. A distribution of intensity, or diffraction pattern, therefore exists in the vicinity of F. The form of this depends on the distribution of the parts of the surface PQ which contribute to it, i.e., on the form of the aperture of the system, but there is no direct correspondence in appearance between the aperture which limits PQ and the pattern appearing on a screen placed anywhere in the beam near F.

Near F the whole area of PQ must be considered as contributing to the amplitude at C. Farther away the phase range and the magnitudes of the contributions from the various parts of PQ become such that the area of PQ well away from R, the foot of the perpendicular from C, makes no contribution. Ultimately only a very small area near R is effective, and the discussion earlier in this section is then applicable. When C is moved in the transverse direction from F, as shown in Fig. 2E, R lies on the continuation of the surface PQ (being actually vertically above C). If PQ represents the full extent of the wave passed by the system the area near R does not form part of this, so that there is no amplitude contribution at C. Thus, on a screen in a transverse plane through F the intensity is zero at appreciable distances from F. Near to F, however, the effect of PQ is not zero, except in some special positions, and a diffraction pattern appears on the screen. This, as has already been suggested, is of smaller dimensions the larger the angular aperture of the wave-front. Rectilinear propagation of light would lead to the expectation of an accurate point image at F. This is evidently more nearly achieved with a wide-aperture system, but, since there must always be some limit to the aperture, is never precisely obtained. Diffraction effects near the focus of a beam of light are known as *Fraunhofer diffraction patterns*. Those in the edges of shadows of obstacles are termed *Fresnel diffraction effects*. The foregoing discussion indicates how one type of effect merges into the other as the points considered are made nearer or farther from the image plane of an optical system.

A fuller account of diffraction effects appears later. The immediately important points which emerge from this preliminary discussion are :

(1) If wide beams of light are considered, the wave-fronts advance in the way predicted by Huygens' construction over almost the whole of their area. The construction fails only very near the edges of the wave-fronts, where they are limited by the apertures of the system. In the remainder of this chapter surfaces of spherical or plane form are considered to represent the central portions only of wave-fronts, so that it is permissible to consider Huygens' principle as applicable to the whole of these surfaces. The behaviour of the central portions of wide beams of light is adequately represented by such considerations, and results in exact agreement with the description of reflection and refraction effects in terms of light " rays " are obtained.

(2) Wave-fronts converging on points, which by Huygens' principle should give point images, can never actually do so, by virtue of the fact that the apertures of systems, even if large, must nevertheless have a definite limit.

Wave description of reflection and refraction effects

Consider a broad parallel beam of light, either from a very distant point source or issuing from some collimating arrangement. The wave-fronts in such a case are planes perpendicular to the direction of the light beam. Let PQ be a portion of a wave-front taken from its central area. According to Huygens' principle, PQ advances, remaining parallel to its original direction. Let the beam approach a plane boundary AB separating two optical media 1 and 2, in the way shown in Fig. 2F. The planes of the wave-fronts and the surface of separation must be imagined perpendicular to the plane of the figure. Let the velocities of light in the two media be c_1 and c_2. When the wave-front reaches the position P_1Q_1 shown, the secondary waves from P_1 thereafter advance entirely in medium 2; but those from other parts of P_1Q_1 have some remaining distance to cover in medium 1 (e.g. G_1 has to go to H). The secondary waves from all parts of P_1Q_1 will have entered medium 2 by the time Q_1 reaches Q_2. The distance covered by P_1 while Q_1 advances to Q_2 is given by $P_1P_2 = \dfrac{c_2}{c_1} \cdot Q_1Q_2$. The secondary wave from P_1 has this radius when that from Q_1 passes through

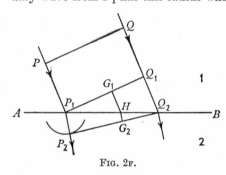

FIG. 2F.

Q_2. The wave-front in medium 2 must be normal to the new direction of propagation; and so is obtained by drawing a tangent plane from Q_2 to the sphere around P_1 having the radius P_1P_2. For any general point on P_1Q_1, such as G_1, the distance G_1H is covered at velocity c_1 and the distance HG_2 at c_2, and it is evident from simple geometrical con-

siderations that this occupies the same time as the movements P_1P_2 and Q_1Q_2 at the extremities of the area considered. The new surface P_2Q_2 is thus tangential to all the secondary waves from P_1Q_1 at this instant.

The angle of incidence is the angle (in the plane of Fig. 2F) between the incident wave surface P_1Q_1 and the refracting surface, since these surfaces are respectively perpendicular to the incident direction and the normal.

Thus $$i_1 = \widehat{Q_1P_1Q_2}$$

and, from a similar argument,

$$i_2 = \widehat{P_1Q_2P_2}$$

Hence $$\frac{\sin i_1}{\sin i_2} = \frac{Q_1Q_2}{P_1P_2} = \frac{c_1}{c_2} \qquad \cdots \quad \cdots \quad 2.1$$

The wave theory thus accounts for Snell's law, and assigns the magnitude c_1/c_2 for the relative refractive index μ. The corpuscular theory

$$1 \to 2$$

of light, advocated by Newton, explained the constancy of $\sin i_1 / \sin i_2$ equally well, but the magnitude predicted was c_2/c_1 instead of c_1/c_2. The velocity of light in water was found by Foucault in 1850 to be less than that in air, and this result in itself afforded some discriminative evidence in favour of the wave theory of light.   Later experiments of higher accuracy, especially those by Michelson using carbon disulphide, have shown that a definite difference exists between the ratio c_1/c_2 and μ.   This, however, may be accounted for by the fact that the direct $1 \to 2$ velocity determinations give the *group velocities*, while the refractive index is the ratio of the *wave* or *phase velocities* in the two media.

The reflection laws may be explained in a similar way, drawing a

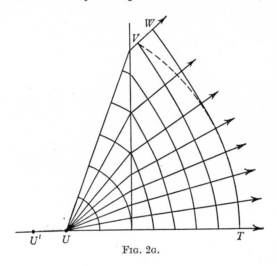

FIG. 2G.

surface around P_1 (Fig. 2F) of radius equal to Q_1Q_2, the secondary waves returning into the first medium at the initial velocity.   The equation 2.1 includes the law of reflection, however, if c_2 is taken as $-c_1$, that is if waves returning at the same velocity from AB are considered.

When a divergent or convergent beam of light is considered, the incident and refracted wave-front surfaces are curved, but any area of small dimensions compared with the radius of such a surface is refracted exactly in the manner already described for a plane wave-front; so that the law of refraction holds for all the incident directions in such a beam.   If an incident beam orginating at a point object is considered, the incident wave-fronts are spherical, but the refracted wave-fronts are distorted from the spherical shape, approximating closely to portions of spheres only when the incident angles are small.   Fig. 2G shows the effect on spherical wave-fronts when they pass from air into a medium

B

of refractive index 1·5 through a plane refracting surface. The curves shown represent successive positions of a wave-front from the point U at regular intervals of time, the distance covered in the medium being two-thirds of that covered in air in the same time. Near the direction perpendicular to the surface, the refracted wave-fronts are to a close approximation spherical around the point U', the paraxial image of U, which is 1·5 times as distant as U from the surface. The wave-front TW, for example, coincides near T with the spherical surface TV, which has its centre at U'. Farther away, the normals to the refracted wave surface pass above U'. It is evident that the aberrations of a system are connected with the non-spherical nature of the wave-fronts which emerge from it. The distance VW, i.e., the separation in any particular direction between the actual front and the ideal one centred on the paraxial image point, is frequently termed the *wave-front aberration* in this particular direction.

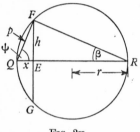

The explanation of aberrations of more complex optical systems, based on this concept, is suggested later in this chapter. At the moment the simple behaviour of systems containing curved refracting or reflecting surfaces remains to be indicated, and attention is confined to the region near the axis where the emergent wave-fronts

FIG. 2H.

may be taken as spherical in form. Paraxial refraction by a thin lens is discussed as a representative example of the description of this type of effect by wave methods.

It is first necessary to establish briefly a geometrical theorem which is used repeatedly in the deduction which follows. In Fig. 2H, QR is a diameter of a circle of radius r and FG a chord which intersects it at right angles at E. The symbols x, h, and p are used for the lengths QE, FE, and QF, and ψ for the angle FQR.

Then
$$\cos \psi = \frac{p}{2r} = \frac{x}{p}$$

i.e.,
$$x = \frac{p^2}{2r}, \quad \text{or} \quad \frac{x}{r} = \frac{h^2 + x^2}{2r^2}$$

In circumstances when x^2/r^2 is negligible, this may be approximated to

$$x = \frac{h^2}{2r} \quad . \quad . \quad . \quad . \quad . \quad . \quad \textbf{2.2}$$

This equation will be used immediately for inclinations such as β in the figure for which first-order approximations are sufficient. It should be noted, however, that it is still applicable when β has magnitudes for which third-order approximations are satisfactory. This is evident since

$$\frac{x}{r} = \frac{p^2}{2r^2} = \tfrac{1}{2} \sin^2\beta$$

so that $\dfrac{x^2}{r^2} \to 0$ when higher than third powers of β may be ignored.

The fact that h may be substituted for p for third-order magnitudes of angles such as β will be used in the next section.

Consider now a thin converging lens in air, the material being of refractive index n, and the radii of the faces r_1 and r_2. For clarity the lens is illustrated with exaggerated thickness in Fig. 2J. Let U and U' be axial object and image points, at distances l and l' from the lens.

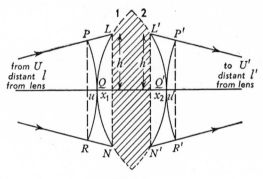

FIG. 2J.

For the present the distance symbols simply represent the numerical magnitudes of the quantities concerned. Waves from U passing through only a restricted central portion of the aperture are considered, the distance h from the axis of any point within this part of the aperture being small relative to the distances r_1, r_2, l, and l'. Thus the inclinations to the axis of all the incident and emergent light directions are small. The approximation involved in the deduction of equation 2.2 is then admissible; also a distance such as PL in the figure may be taken as the longitudinal separation of P and L, since the cosine of the small angle made by PL with the axial direction may be taken as unity. PQR represents a spherical wave-front from U at the moment when it first touches the lens, at Q. The portions of this wave-front away from Q have, at this instant, some remaining path to cover in air before entering the lens. Because the lens is thicker on the axis than elsewhere, the parts of the wave-front near the axis traverse longer paths in the lens than those more remote from the axis. Since the velocity in air is n times that in the medium, the curvature of the wave-front must be altered by passage through the lens. While Q covers the distance QQ' within the lens, the larger distance $PLL'P'$ is covered by P, part of this path being in air. The converging effect of this kind of lens is thus explained.

All parts of the emergent wave-front $P'Q'R'$ must have the same phase as was common to the surface PQR at an earlier instant. The time interval occupied in the passage of any element of PQR through the lens to its new position in $P'Q'R'$ must therefore be the same every-where. Since a distance equal to LL' within the lens is traversed by all parts of the wave-front, it suffices to equate the times taken by the various parts in covering the rest of their paths excluding this distance. Thus P covers PL and $L'P'$ in air, in addition to LL' within the lens ; Q covers x_1 and x_2 in the lens, in addition to LL'. The distance covered in air in any time is n times that covered in the lens. The condition that the time taken should be constant is that the equivalent distances *in air* (or, more precisely, in a vacuum) should be alike. These equi-valent distances are known as the *optical paths* taken by the light. Equating these optical paths in this case

$$PL + L'P' = n(x_1 + x_2)$$

but $$PL = u + x_1$$
and $$P'L' = u' + x_2$$
Hence $$u + u' = (n - 1)(x_1 + x_2)$$

and, using equation 2.2,

$$\frac{h^2}{2}\left(\frac{1}{l} + \frac{1}{l'}\right) = (n-1)\frac{h^2}{2}\left(\frac{1}{r_1} + \frac{1}{r_2}\right)$$

or $$\left(\frac{1}{l} + \frac{1}{l'}\right) = (n-1)\left(\frac{1}{r_1} + \frac{1}{r_2}\right) \quad . \quad . \quad . \quad 2.3$$

This equation relates the numerical magnitudes of the distances con-cerned in the special case considered. It may be generalized by intro-duction of a sign convention. If, for example, the New Cartesian con-vention is adopted, the distances to the left of the lens in Fig. 2J must be considered negative. When the symbols include the signs of the quantities, the above equation may be written in the general form :

$$\left(\frac{1}{l'} - \frac{1}{l}\right) = (n-1)\left(\frac{1}{r_1} - \frac{1}{r_2}\right) \quad . \quad . \quad . \quad 2.4$$

The deduction of this equation, obtainable also by well-known geo-metrical methods, sufficiently indicates how this type of behaviour of optical systems is explained equally well by wave-optical methods.

Wave theory and aberrations

The immediately preceding discussion was confined to circumstances in which the entrant and emergent waves were spherical, i.e., point images were produced from point objects. The assumption involved, so that this may be true, was that the angles of inclination to the axis of the wave normals at any parts of the wave-fronts were always quite small, so that first-order approximations (such as $\sin \theta \simeq \theta$ and $\cos \theta \simeq 1$) were permissible.

Outside this range of inclinations point images are no longer produced, the emergent wave-fronts being no longer spherical in shape, as has been indicated in a rather special case in Fig. 2G. This is because the optical paths through any optical system from U to U' along the directions more inclined to the axis are not constant, as they are in the

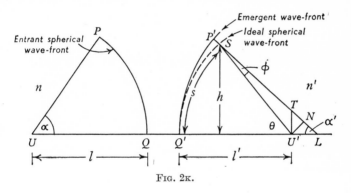

FIG. 2K.

paraxial region. Fig. 2K illustrates a case in which the outer optical paths are longer than the paraxial ones. If the optical paths from U to U' were all equal, the emergent wave-front would at some instant be in the spherical surface $Q'S$ around U', but the actual wave-front coincides with this surface only near Q' and lies behind it elsewhere. The amount by which the optical path $UPP'U'$ is longer than $UQQ'U'$ approximates closely when the aberration is small to $P'S$, the separation along the wave normal of the actual and ideal wave surfaces. If the waves emerge into a medium of refractive index n', the optical path difference is n' times the geometric length $P'S$. Let Q' be the second principal point of the system, so that $Q'U' = l'$. Let v represent the length $P'S$, and w the corresponding optical path $(n'v)$, and let h be the height of S above the axis, and s the length of the arc $Q'S$. Since U and U' are axial points and a centred system symmetrical about its axis is under consideration, the emergent wave-front must also be symmetrical about this axis. The normals $P'SL$ and SU'

to the actual and ideal wave-fronts therefore lie in the same plane, the plane of Fig. 2K. This will not necessarily occur when off-axial object points are considered. The small angle ϕ between the normals $P'SL$ and SU' must equal the angle between the tangent planes to the two surfaces at the points P' and S. This is clearly $\dfrac{dv}{ds}$.

Thus,
$$\phi = \frac{1}{n'} \cdot \frac{dw}{ds}$$

Let $U'N$ be drawn perpendicular to $P'SL$.

Then
$$U'N = l'\phi = \frac{l'}{n'} \cdot \frac{dw}{ds} = \frac{1}{n'} \cdot \frac{dw}{d\theta}$$

Now, since ϕ is small, $\alpha' \simeq \theta$ (see Fig. 2K)

and
$$TU' = \frac{U'N}{\cos\theta} = \frac{1}{n'} \cdot \frac{dw}{d(\sin\theta)} = \frac{l'}{n'} \cdot \frac{dw}{dh} \quad \cdots \quad \textbf{2.5}$$

while
$$LU' = \frac{U'N}{\sin\theta} = \frac{l'^2}{hn'} \cdot \frac{dw}{ds} \quad \cdots \cdots \cdots \quad \textbf{2.6}$$

By use of these equations the transverse and longitudinal aberrations are deducible from the form of the wave-front, in circumstances in which the angular aberration (ϕ) is small.

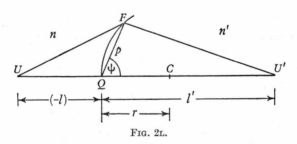

FIG. 2L.

The wave-front aberration is usually considered negative when the actual wave-front is behind the ideal one, as is the case in Fig. 2K. The wave normal at P' then intersects the axis at L to the right of the paraxial image U'. The longitudinal aberration is normally given the negative sign when this is the case, so that the signs allotted to the two measures of the aberration are consistent.

An indication will now be given of the explanation of the spherical aberration of a single spherical refracting surface, and of the way in which the argument may be extended to account for the other Seidelian aberrations.

Let FQ (Fig. 2L) be a spherical refracting surface of radius r separating media of refractive index n and n'. Let U and U' be two paraxially conjugate points on the axis, their distances being l and l' from Q. The New Cartesian convention is introduced immediately, so that the argument is general for any curvature of the surface and any object position. U being to the left of the surface in the case drawn, the numerical magnitude of UQ is $(-l)$. The difference in optical path w between the waves travelling from U to U' by F and those travelling by Q is

$$w = (nUF + n'FU') - (nUQ + n'QU')$$

Let
$$FQ = p \text{ and } F\widehat{Q}U' = \psi$$

so that
$$\cos \psi = p/2r \text{ (see Fig. 2H)}$$

$$UF^2 = UQ^2 + FQ^2 + 2UQ \cdot FQ \cos \psi$$

$$= l^2 + p^2\left(1 - \frac{l}{r}\right)$$

and
$$UF = -l\left[1 + \frac{p^2}{l^2}\left(1 - \frac{l}{r}\right)\right]^{\frac{1}{2}}$$

The negative sign must be chosen, since this is a distance to the left of the surface.

Similarly

$$FU' = +l'\left[1 + \frac{p^2}{l'^2}\left(1 - \frac{l'}{r}\right)\right]^{\frac{1}{2}}$$

Expanding by the binomial theorem and substituting into the expression for w :

$$w = \frac{p^2}{2}\left[n'\left(\frac{1}{l'} - \frac{1}{r}\right) - n\left(\frac{1}{l} - \frac{1}{r}\right)\right]$$
$$- \frac{p^4}{8}\left[\frac{n'}{l'}\left(\frac{1}{l'} - \frac{1}{r}\right)^2 - \frac{n}{l}\left(\frac{1}{l} - \frac{1}{r}\right)^2\right]$$
$$+ \text{ terms containing } p^6, p^8, \text{ etc.} \quad . \quad . \quad . \quad \textbf{2.7}$$

In the paraxial region the p^4 and higher terms are negligible and the condition that U and U' are paraxially conjugate is that w is zero, which is the case when

$$\frac{n'}{l'} - \frac{n}{l} = \frac{n' - n}{r} \qquad . \quad . \quad . \quad . \quad \textbf{2.8}$$

Equation 2.8 is well known in geometrical optics as the conjugate distance relation for a single spherical surface. Its proof is an incidental outcome of this consideration of aberrations by wave methods.

When higher than third-order aberrations may be neglected the p^6 and higher terms in equation 2.7 may be ignored. In the previous section it was shown that h, the perpendicular distance of F from the axis, is a sufficient substitute for p (or s) under these circumstances. Equation 2.7 then becomes

$$w = -\frac{h^4}{8}\left[\frac{n'}{l'}\left(\frac{1}{l'} - \frac{1}{r}\right)^2 - \frac{n}{l}\left(\frac{1}{l} - \frac{1}{r}\right)^2\right] \quad . \quad . \quad . \quad 2.9$$

Using equations 2.5 and 2.6, the transverse and longitudinal spherical aberrations deduced from this expression are :

$$TU' = \frac{l'h^3}{2n'}\left[\frac{n'}{l'}\left(\frac{1}{l'} - \frac{1}{r}\right)^2 - \frac{n}{l}\left(\frac{1}{l} - \frac{1}{r}\right)^2\right]$$

and

$$LU' = \frac{l'^2h^2}{2n'}\left[\frac{n'}{l'}\left(\frac{1}{l'} - \frac{1}{r}\right)^2 - \frac{n}{l}\left(\frac{1}{l} - \frac{1}{r}\right)^2\right]$$

The dependence of these aberrations on the aperture radius h and the particular conjugate distances concerned is made clear by these expressions. Generally, when the higher terms of equation 2.7 cannot be ignored, other terms involving higher powers of h appear in addition in the expressions for TU' and LU'.

Equation 2.9, which is applicable to third-order aberrations, may be written simply as

$$w = k \, . \, h^4 \quad . \quad . \quad . \quad . \quad . \quad . \quad 2.10$$

k being a constant for a particular object position relative to the surface. This equation will now be used to indicate the extension of this type of argument to account for the other Seidel aberrations.

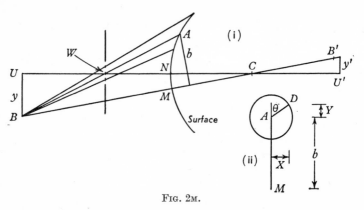

Fig. 2m.

Fig. 2m (i) shows a single refracting surface AM, with an aperture some distance in front of it, having its centre at W. This aperture acts as the entrance pupil of the system. An off-axial object point B is now considered, and the line BC is the auxiliary axis of the surface with respect to this point. The line BW is the direction of advance of the waves through the centre of the entrance pupil, usually termed the principal ray in geometrical optics, and A is the point of incidence of this ray upon the surface. B' is the point conjugate with B by refraction of paraxial rays about the auxiliary axis, and b is the height of A perpendicularly above this axis.

In addition to the principal ray consider also those incident directions passed by one circular zone around W in the entrance pupil. These will fall on the surface at points on a circle around A. This is only approximately a circle, but the approximation is satisfactory, since for third-order aberrations distances such as b are interchangeable with distances along the curved surface. Fig. 2M (ii) indicates the surface from the front, and shows the circle around A and its position relative to M, the point of intersection of the auxiliary axis with the surface. Let D be a point on this circle. If w represents the wavefront aberration for refraction occurring at D its magnitude may be stated as follows, using equation 2.10

$$w = k \cdot (MD)^4$$

If X and Y are the co-ordinates of D (relative to A as origin) perpendicular to and parallel to the tangential plane, it is clear from Fig. 2M (ii) that

$$MD^2 = (b + Y)^2 + X^2$$

Thus

$$w = k[(X^2 + Y^2)^2 + 4bY(X^2 + Y^2) + 2b^2(X^2 + 3Y^2) + 4b^3Y + b^4]$$

The term kb^4 is the wave-front aberration for waves through the centre W of the aperture, and the symbol w_A may be used as an alternative for this term. The transverse aberration in the plane through B', perpendicular to the auxiliary axis, is given by equation 2.5, and its components T_X and T_Y parallel to X and Y, will be given by

$$T_X = \frac{l'}{n'} \cdot \frac{dw}{dX} \quad \text{and} \quad T_Y = \frac{l'}{n'} \cdot \frac{dw}{dY}$$

Also b in the above expression is directly proportional to y the object distance from the axis. This is evident from Fig. 2M (i), since the portions AN and NM are each directly proportional to y. The results of differentiation of the above expression for w may thus be written in the forms :

$$T_X = \frac{l'}{n'} [\alpha X(X^2 + Y^2) + 2\beta XYy + \gamma Xy^2]$$

and $\quad T_Y = \dfrac{l'}{n'} [\alpha Y(X^2 + Y^2) + \beta(X^2 + 3Y^2)y + 3\gamma Yy^2 + \phi y^3]$

In these expressions α, β, γ, and ϕ are constants.

Using polar co-ordinates such that $X = r \sin \theta$ and $Y = r \cos \theta$, where r is the distance AD of Fig. 2M (ii) (which is directly proportional to the radius of the zone of the entrance pupil through which the rays considered pass) these expressions may be written :

$$w - w_A = \tfrac{1}{4}\alpha r^4 + \beta r^3(\cos \theta)y + \tfrac{1}{2}\gamma r^2(2 + \cos 2\theta)y^2 + \phi r(\cos \theta)y^3$$

$$T_X = \frac{l'}{n'}\left[\alpha r^3 \sin \theta + \beta r^2(\sin 2\theta)y + \gamma r(\sin \theta)y^2\right]$$

$$T_Y = \frac{l'}{n'}\left[\alpha r^3 \cos \theta + \beta r^2(2 + \cos 2\theta)y + 3\gamma r(\cos \theta)y^2 + \phi y^3\right]$$

The separate terms in these expressions are the contributions due to aberrations of the various types; the α, β, γ, and ϕ terms corresponding respectively to spherical aberration, coma, astigmatism, and distortion. The familiar forms taken by each of these aberrations in the absence of others may be shown from the expressions for T_X and T_Y by ignoring all terms not containing α, β, γ, and ϕ in turn.

SPHERICAL ABERRATION

Ignoring the β, γ, and ϕ terms and eliminating θ from the expressions for T_X and T_Y

$$T_X{}^2 + T_Y{}^2 = (\text{constant} \times r^3)^2$$

Thus for rays through all points such as D in Fig. 2M (ii) the intersection points with the plane perpendicular to the auxiliary axis through B' lie on a circle having B' as centre. The radius of this circle is normally known as the lateral spherical aberration, and is proportional to the cube of the radius of the zone of the aperture through which the rays pass.

COMA

Ignoring all but the β terms and eliminating θ

$$\left(\frac{T_Y}{C} - 2\right)^2 + \left(\frac{T_X}{C}\right)^2 = 1$$

where

$$C = \frac{l'}{n'}\beta r^2 y$$

This equation represents a circular image in the transverse plane through B'. The radius of the circle is C, and its centre is displaced $2C$ from B' in the tangential plane. This is the well-known form of the comatic image of an off-axial point formed by a single zone of the aperture of a system, and C is the sagittal coma. C is seen to be proportional to r^2 and to y, i.e., to the square of the aperture radius and the first power of the field.

It should be noted that since both the β terms in T_X and T_Y contain 2θ, the whole of the comatic ring focus is produced by a semicircle only in the zone of the aperture through which the rays pass. Any one point on the ring focus is the focusing point of two rays through diametrically opposite points in the zone of the aperture.

ASTIGMATISM

Consideration of the γ terms in the same way yields the expression

$$T_X{}^2 + \left(\frac{T_Y}{3}\right)^2 = (\text{constant} \times ry^2)^2$$

which is an ellipse with B' at its centre, the major axis being in the tangential plane and three times the length of the minor axis. This is the well-known form of the section of an astigmatic beam beyond the tangential and sagittal line images. Since the convergence on the beam from one aperture zone may be considered constant in the region of focus, it is evident that the tangential rays have crossed in front of this elliptical image at a point three times as distant as the intersection point of the sagittal rays. The dependence of the third-order lateral astigmatism on the square of the field and the first power of the aperture is clear from the equation for the elliptical image.

DISTORTION

The ϕ term appears only in the expression for T_Y and does not involve r

$$T_Y = \text{constant} \times y^3$$

This represents a transverse displacement from the paraxial image point B', proportional to the cube of the field, which remains the same for all points in the aperture for any fixed position of B in the object field.

PETZVAL CURVATURE

This does not arise in the same way as the above-mentioned aberrations. The point B' (Fig. 2M (i)) formed by refraction of paraxial rays about the auxiliary axis BC, does not generally lie in the same plane as U', and the image $U'B'$ is curved. This is purely a consequence of the fact that B is slightly further (in the case illustrated) from the surface than U, and of the application of paraxial considerations to the two object distances BM and UN. Its explanation by wave methods is thus satisfactorily achieved by accounting for the paraxial relation. This has been done previously in this section (see equation 2.8).

CHAPTER 3

DIFFRACTION AND INTERFERENCE
OF WAVES

As an introduction to the basic terms and principles of interference and diffraction phenomena, the superposition of the wave systems from two sources or apertures of negligible dimensions was discussed in Chapter 1, with a brief indication only of the extension of these ideas to more general and practical cases. In Chapter 2 the justification of Huygens' construction, by application of the same principle of superposition to all the secondary disturbances arising at the various parts of an advancing wave-front, was indicated. It was necessary to imagine wave-fronts not restricted by any obstacles or apertures in order to account for propagation along normals to the wave-fronts everywhere over their area; diffraction effects were seen to be the outcome of restrictions imposed on the wave-fronts, the manner in which these arise being discussed only briefly and qualitatively. The examples so far discussed have therefore been of an idealized kind chosen mainly to emphasize the underlying principles, which may not be realized with actual optical systems, since the apertures used can neither be so small as to transmit areas of wave-fronts of negligible dimensions, nor so large as to impose absolutely no restrictions on the wave-fronts which they transmit.

The present chapter and the following one are concerned with examples of effects occurring when the transmitted portions of the incident wave-fronts are neither negligible nor very large in area. The selection from amongst the many effects of this nature made in this chapter is not a very representative one, the examples chosen being of a rather special kind within the broad class known as Fraunhofer diffraction phenomena. More varied effects, of both the Fraunhofer and Fresnel types, are mentioned in the next chapter. The discussion of this chapter is mainly devoted to the effects of Fraunhofer diffraction at a single slit, a pair of slits, and several regularly spaced slits; these are of considerable practical importance and also simple to account for mathematically. In addition, an account of these is useful in order to clarify the distinction between interference and diffraction effects, and at the same time to emphasize the common basic principles underlying both types of phenomenon.

Fraunhofer diffraction by a single slit

(i) **Plane incident waves.**—Fig. 3A shows a single slit of breadth a illuminated by a parallel beam of light falling normally on the screen containing the slit. Plane waves are therefore incident on the aperture; in the simplest arrangement these may arrive directly from some distant point object. For the present, effects in the plane of the figure only are considered. Any one wave-front reaches the plane of the screen containing the slit everywhere at the same instant, and the effect anywhere beyond the screen is that of superposition there of the secondary waves from the parts of the wave-front which are not obstructed. Attention is confined to points at considerable distance from the slit compared with its breadth, so that the directions from all parts of the breadth of the slit to any such point may be considered parallel. This really restricts the discussion to Fraunhofer diffraction

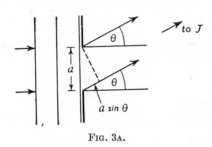

FIG. 3A.

of plane waves. As already mentioned, Fraunhofer diffraction effects occur near the foci of beams of light, i.e., near the plane conjugate with the object plane. The present case is a rather special one of this kind in which the object is distant and, there being no focusing elements in the optical system, the image plane where the Fraunhofer phenomena appear is also at infinity. Effects of introducing lenses will be mentioned later.

Consider the secondary waves advancing in some direction making an angle θ with the continuation of the incident direction. The path difference, in this direction, between waves originating at the top and bottom of the slit is $a \sin \theta$. The amplitude contributions from the extreme top and bottom elements of the area of the slit therefore differ in phase by $\frac{2\pi}{\lambda} a \sin \theta$, or 2β. The elements of area are parallel to the length of the slit, and, lying side by side, together make up its full area. They are all similar, and the phases of the contributions at some distant point in the direction θ vary continuously and uniformly as the slit is traversed. The phase-amplitude diagram is therefore an arc of a circle, the tangents at its extremities being inclined at the angle 2β. This is indicated in Fig. 3B (i); OA is the circular arc, and the chord OA, of magnitude R_1, is the resultant amplitude. When $\theta = 0$, i.e., in the direction which is the continuation forward of the incident direction, the diagram takes the simple form shown in Fig. 3B (ii).

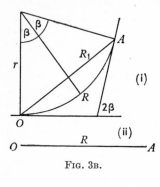

Here the contributions from all the elements of area are in phase, so that their amplitudes simply add numerically to give R, the total amplitude in this direction. The separate small amplitudes, which together form the straight line OA in Fig. 3B (ii), are progressively inclined to one another when $\theta \neq 0$, lying on the curve OA of Fig. 3B (i). The arc of the circle in this figure therefore has the length R, which is the total resultant amplitude in the directly forward direction.

Fig. 3B.

Drawing the radii of the arc OA at the points O and A (Fig. 3B (i)) and putting r equal to the radius of this arc

$$R_1 = 2r \sin \beta$$
and
$$R = 2r\beta$$
Hence
$$\frac{R_1}{R} = \frac{\sin \beta}{\beta}$$

Since the intensities depend on the squares of the amplitudes, this may be written

$$\frac{I_1}{I} = \frac{\sin^2 \beta}{\beta^2} . \qquad \qquad \textbf{3.1}$$

where I_1 and I are the corresponding intensities. The variations with β of $\sin \beta$, $\dfrac{\sin \beta}{\beta}$, and $\dfrac{\sin^2 \beta}{\beta^2}$ are illustrated in Fig. 3c (i), (ii), and (iii). Zero amplitude and intensity occur in directions such that $\beta = \pm m\pi$, m being any integer (but not zero). The corresponding θ values are given by $\sin \theta = \pm \dfrac{m\lambda}{a}$. These are the directions of zero intensity, the general intensity distribution being as indicated in Fig. 3c (iii); it is clear that the pattern is spread over a larger angular extent the finer the slit used.

The maxima are in positions not exactly intermediate between the minima. Putting $\dfrac{d}{d\beta}\left(\dfrac{\sin \beta}{\beta}\right) = 0$, the condition for the maxima resulting is $\tan \beta = \beta$. The corresponding β values are 0, $1\cdot43\pi$, $2\cdot46\pi$, $3\cdot47\pi$, ... etc.

Lenses may be introduced on both sides of the aperture to obviate the necessity of using a distant source and of viewing the effects at a large distance from the aperture. A collimating lens with a source at its first focal point produces an incident beam similar to that considered above. The diffracted parallel beams, of different intensities in different directions, may be focused by a further lens beyond the slit; the focused pattern then appearing in the second focal plane of the lens.

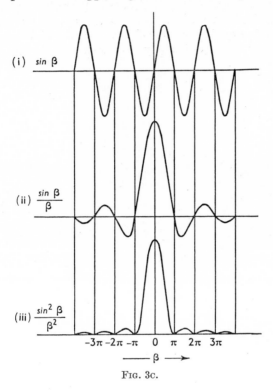

(i) $\sin \beta$

(ii) $\dfrac{\sin \beta}{\beta}$

(iii) $\dfrac{\sin^2 \beta}{\beta^2}$

$-3\pi\ -2\pi\ -\pi \qquad 0 \qquad \pi \quad 2\pi \quad 3\pi$

$\beta \longrightarrow$

Fig. 3c.

In the absence of the slit the lens arrangement would simply focus an image of the object point into this plane.

The diffraction due to the breadth a of the slit occurs in the direction parallel to the dimension a, and is appreciable because a is small. Assuming a comparatively long slit, no appreciable diffraction occurs in the direction parallel to the length of the slit. A line object may therefore be used, in place of the point object so far discussed, the line being placed parallel to the slit. In the absence of the diffracting slit the lens arrangement would produce an image which in the absence of aberrations due to the lenses would be similar to the object line. With the diffracting slit inserted, every point of this line image would be spread out in the direction perpendicular to its length, the distribution of intensity along any line perpendicular to the image being as suggested by Fig. 3c (iii).

(ii) **Spherical incident waves.**—A focused diffraction pattern due to a single slit inserted between two lenses in such a way that parallel incident beams fall upon it, was discussed at the close of the previous paragraph. The same type of pattern is formed, however, and its explanation follows similar lines, when the aperture is inserted parallel to the object slit *anywhere* in the system which produces a focused image

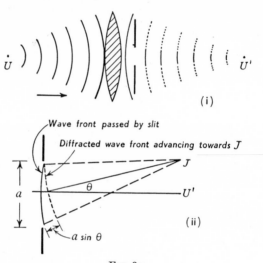

FIG. 3D.

of the object. It may generally be inserted in a part of the system where the light is converging or diverging, that is to say the incident wave-fronts are not plane but spherical. As a more general example of Fraunhofer diffraction, the arrangement of Fig. 3D (i) may be considered. Here the single lens converges the waves from the object at U towards the image U', but a diffraction pattern rather than a true image appears at U' because of the interposition of the slit aperture behind the lens, where the waves are converging. Fig. 3D (ii) shows the diagram which corresponds to Fig. 3A in this case. At any point J, laterally displaced by a small amount from U' and sufficiently distant compared with the breadth of the slit, the difference in path to J from the two extremities of the slit is $a \sin \theta$. This corresponds to a range of phases of the amplitude contributions at J, due to the various parts of the breadth of the slit, equal to $\dfrac{2\pi}{\lambda} a \sin \theta$(or 2β); and by arguments exactly similar to those used previously the intensity in direction θ is measured by $\sin^2\!\beta/\beta^2$. A similar argument may be used when the slit is on the object side of the lens. The waves incident upon it are then diverging (i.e., convex) and the diffracted diverging waves are focused by the lens into a similar pattern in the image plane.

Fraunhofer diffraction by a double slit

The discussion commenced in the previous section by consideration of plane incident and diffracted waves was later shown to be applicable also to spherical waves, effects of the same form then being obtained in the image plane of the system. It will therefore suffice to discuss plane waves only in the remaining sections of this chapter, bearing in mind the similar nature of the effects produced when focused systems are used.

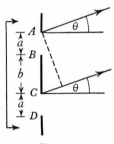

Fig. 3E shows two parallel slits AB, CD, each of breadth a, the opaque strip between them having breadth b. Plane waves are incident in a direction normal to the screen containing the slits, and effects in the direction θ to the directly forward direction are considered. The phase-amplitude diagram for either of the slits separately is similar to

FIG. 3E.

Fig. 3B (i). That for both of the slits together consists of two similar arcs, each a portion of the circumference of the same circle, spaced apart on the circumference of the circle because of the intervening opaque strip between the slits. Corresponding parts of the slits (e.g., the topmost parts in each of the slits) are separated by the distance $(a + b)$; hence the waves in the direction θ from corresponding parts of the two slits differ in phase by $\dfrac{2\pi}{\lambda} (a + b) \sin \theta$. The symbol δ was used for this phase difference in Chapter 1 in the discussion of the similar case in which the slit breadths were neglected, and is used again here. It is convenient also to use the symbol γ for $\delta/2$.

Thus
$$\delta = 2\gamma = \frac{2\pi}{\lambda} (a + b) \sin \theta$$

The phase-amplitude diagram appears in Fig. 3F (i), the points A, B, C and D on the circular arc corresponding to the amplitude contributions from the similarly lettered parts of the slit system in Fig. 3E. The points C and A are the topmost points of the two slits, and the radii of the circular arcs through C and A (in Fig. 3F (i)) are separated by the angle 2γ, since the amplitude components in the directions of the tangents at C and A differ in phase by 2γ. It is clear that the two chords of length R_1 represent the separate resultant amplitudes in the direction θ from the separate slits. Each of these is $R \cdot \dfrac{\sin \beta}{\beta}$, where R is the resultant amplitude from one slit in the direction $\theta = 0$, and they clearly also differ in phase by 2γ. The phase-amplitude diagram for summation of these is Fig. 3F (ii), and the total resultant amplitude R_2 from both slits is given by

$$R_2{}^2 = 2R_1{}^2 (1 + \cos 2\gamma)$$

or $$R_2 = 2R_1 \cos \gamma = 2R \cdot \frac{\sin \beta}{\beta} \cdot \cos \gamma$$

The resultant amplitude in the direction $\theta = 0$ due to both the slits is $2R$, and the intensity I in this direction is proportional to the square of

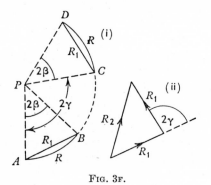

FIG. 3F.

this. The intensity I_2 in any general direction θ is proportional to $R_2{}^2$.

Thus $$\frac{I_2}{I} = \frac{\sin^2 \beta}{\beta^2} \cdot \cos^2 \gamma \qquad \cdot \quad \cdot \quad \cdot \quad \cdot \quad \cdot \quad 3.2$$

where $$\beta = \frac{\pi}{\lambda} a \sin \theta, \quad \text{and} \quad \gamma = \frac{\pi}{\lambda} (a + b) \sin \theta.$$

The forms of $\dfrac{\sin^2 \beta}{\beta^2}$, and of $\cos^2 \gamma \left(\text{or} \cos^2 \dfrac{\delta}{2} \right)$, appear separately in Figs. 3C (iii) and 1E (ii). The form of the product of these two quantities is of the type shown in Fig. 3G. Intensity maxima occur in directions where $\cos^2 \gamma$ has maximum values, i.e., in the directions for which $(a + b) \sin \theta = m\lambda$. This is exactly as in the example discussed in Chapter 1, where the slit breadths were neglected. The maxima are not equally intense in this case, however, since the whole $\cos^2 \gamma$ distribution is modulated by the $\dfrac{\sin^2 \beta}{\beta^2}$ term.

Consider the special circumstances in which the ratio $(a + b)/a$ is an integer, and let this integer be p, so that $\gamma = p\beta$. The zero values of $\dfrac{\sin^2 \beta}{\beta^2}$ occur when β is an integral multiple of π, e.g., $m\pi$. The corresponding value of γ is then $pm\pi$, which is also an integral multiple of π, and therefore represents a maximum in the value of $\cos^2 \gamma$. Such a maximum will be missing from the intensity distribution, since it occurs in a direction in which no light advances, because of the form of the diffraction pattern caused by the separate apertures. Thus the orders which are integral multiples of p are absent from a diffraction

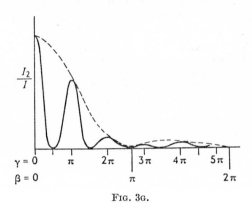

FIG. 3G.

pattern of this nature. For example, if $b = 2a$, p is 3 and the 3rd, 6th, etc., orders are missing. The curve of Fig. 3G shows what occurs more generally when p is not an integer. The curve drawn corresponds to a p value rather less than 3, and the first minimum in $\dfrac{\sin^2 \beta}{\beta^2}$ occurs nearer the $\theta = 0$ direction than the third maximum of $\cos^2 \gamma$.

Discussion of the terms interference and diffraction

The pattern caused by an aperture containing several slits clearly requires consideration next, but this is deferred to the following section, since the examples so far mentioned in this chapter provide a sufficient basis for a more thorough discussion of the terms interference and diffraction than has been possible in earlier pages; this matter is probably best elucidated at as early a stage as possible.

The distinction between the types of phenomenon referred to by the separate terms interference and diffraction is not of a fundamental character. Both are manifestations of the effect of superposition of wave systems from coherent sources. Diffraction of light is probably best considered as a term which describes any departure from strict rectilinear propagation of light, and in Chapter 2 it has been explained how this is caused by the restrictions on the wave-fronts transmitted by optical systems, because of which the combined effect of all the coherent sources in a wave-front passed by the aperture of a system is not zero in all directions other than the original wave-normals. It is therefore correct to describe all the effects discussed in this chapter (and in the next) as pure diffraction effects. In the majority of examples mentioned in this chapter, for instance, the light incident in a direction normal to the screen containing the aperture or apertures is distributed unevenly over a range of directions after passing the screen. Where the aperture is a complex one, however, consisting of two or more separate transparent areas, it is possible to consider the formation of the pattern in a different way. It was, for instance, possible to explain the result obtained with a double slit by considering each slit as producing a diffracted beam (of the form indicated by expression 3.1), the combined effect of both of these beams in any direction then giving the total intensity in that direction. The resultant intensity in certain particular directions, in which each aperture separately produces a definite intensity, may nevertheless be zero, since the displacements in the two wave systems may be just out of phase. Essentially, this method of considering the double-slit pattern divides the action of the complex aperture into two parts. Each aperture provides a light beam varying in intensity with direction; the amplitudes in the separate beams, at any field point, add vectorially to give the resultant amplitude there. On this view diffraction occurs at the separate apertures, and the diffracted beams are then said to interfere. This way of considering this particular problem is in all respects equivalent to the treatment which, considering the problem as one of diffraction alone, simply adds vectorially the disturbances from all the parts of the transmitted wave-front taken as a whole, however complex in fact it may be.

In Fig. 1B, two sources of negligible dimensions compared with light wavelengths were considered. This is a simple, though imaginary, example of pure interference. By imagining sources of this nature the diffraction contribution to the intensity pattern is not considered, since any source of this ideal kind would emit light equally in all forward radial directions, i.e., in a manner consistent with rectilinear propagation. The interference pattern is the result of vectorial addition, at all points, of the displacements in these two wave systems; and, considering the effect as a whole, there is even here a sense in which non-rectilinear propagation effects may be said to occur. Any point where the resultant amplitude is zero, for instance, is not illuminated by the pair of sources, though it is illuminated by either of the sources acting singly. There is obvious inconsistency in speaking of rectilinear propagation when such points, though directly in the path of both beams, are nevertheless not illuminated.

The example first referred to cannot be realized in practice. In practical cases each of the separate interfering beams has diffraction characteristics, even in the absence of the other (or others); though these diffraction characteristics may often be not nearly so prominent as they are in the double-slit intensity pattern discussed in the previous section. Many, though not all, devices designed to exhibit or utilize the interference aspect of these superposition phenomena do so in a manner which effectively excludes diffraction effects, since the diffraction characteristics of the beams occur in small outer regions of the field which are not under observation. A simple example will illustrate this.

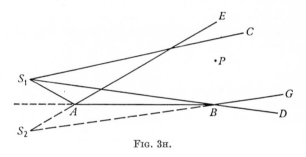

Fig. 3h.

Fig. 3H shows the principle of the Lloyd single-mirror method of production of interference fringes. For clarity the figure is much exaggerated in the direction perpendicular to the plane mirror AB. The single source S_1, which is a fine slit perpendicular to the figure illuminated from behind by monochromatic light, emits light within a range of directions, e.g., within the angle AS_1C. In actuality, diffraction occurs at the slit, and the bounding directions are not sharp for reasons discussed in Chapter 2. The part of the beam within the angle AS_1B is reflected by the mirror roughly within the directions AE and BG. Diffraction effects at the mirror edges also contribute to make the limits of the reflected beam somewhat ill-defined. The reflected beam seems to originate at the virtual source S_2, and illuminates all points above the mirror within the angle ES_2G. Also all points within the angle CS_1D are illuminated directly from S_1. At points within both these angles, such as P, the possibility of interference exists. If the angles CS_1D and ES_2G are appreciable, rectilinear propagation may be considered as occurring over all parts of the areas of the direct and reflected wave-fronts, except those near the diffuse limiting directions of these beams. Thus, for positions of P as shown in the figure (between, but not too near, the lines S_1C and S_2G) no diffraction effects complicate the interference pattern and, provided the pattern is viewed only in such positions, effects which may be considered as entirely interference effects will be viewed.   The range of such positions extends over almost the whole region in which any effects are observable at all.

Summarizing, the distinction between the two kinds of effect, in so far as it is a real one, may be made in the following way:

Diffraction effects are always the result of superposition of an infinite number of wave systems from all the elemental portions of the wave-front transmitted by the aperture or apertures of the system concerned. The phase-amplitude diagram is therefore always a smooth curve, and may take various forms according to the case considered.   Diverse examples are given in this and the following chapter.

Interference effects occur when the aperture of the system contains two or more distinct transparent portions, or the system is composed in such a way that two or more light beams, originally from the same source, traverse some common region of their path.   The essential for interference is thus a limited number of separate beams, each of which may be of complex intensity distribution, controlled to a greater or less extent by diffraction effects.

Rectilinear propagation is accounted for by application of considerations such as are used in explaining diffraction effects (i.e., the superposition of the effects due to all parts of the transmitted area of a wave-front) to unrestricted wave-fronts.   In so far as apertures used in apparatus to produce interference effects are large, and observations are made in regions in the interfering beams where diffraction effects are unlikely to occur (i.e., away from the boundaries of any of the beams, and also away from points where focusing of any of the beams occurs) interference phenomena without appreciable diffraction effects may be obtained.

Fraunhofer diffraction by N regularly spaced slits

An arrangement having several regularly spaced slits forms a simple type of grating.   If the slits are of breadth a and the intervening opaque strips of breadth b, the quantity $(a + b)$ is termed the grating interval. When the number of apertures is N the phase-amplitude diagram may be drawn in a similar manner to that already described for two slits. This is shown in Fig. 3J (i), and consists of N equal arcs equally spaced on the circumference of a circle.   Each arc is of length R and subtends an angle 2β at the centre of the circle. Any chord, of length R_1, corresponding to one of these arcs, is inclined at an angle 2γ to the next

similar chord. The summation of the N resultant amplitudes due to
the separate apertures is represented in Fig. 3J (ii). The point S is
the intersection of the lines which bisect perpendicularly all the lines
of length R_1, and it is clear that any one of these lines R_1 subtends an
angle 2γ at S. The angle subtended at S by the total resultant ampli-

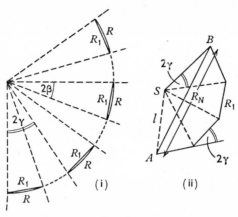

FIG. 3J.

tude R_N, which is the closing side of AB of the polygon, is thus $2N\gamma$.
If AS is denoted by l it is clear that

$$R_1 = 2l \sin \gamma$$

and

$$R_N = 2l \sin N\gamma$$

Thus

$$R_N = R_1 \frac{\sin N\gamma}{\sin \gamma} = R \frac{\sin \beta}{\beta} \cdot \frac{\sin N\gamma}{\sin \gamma}$$

The amplitude in the direction $\theta = 0$ is NR, since each aperture
contributes R, and in this direction the amplitude contributions are all
in phase. The intensity I is thus proportional to $(NR)^2$, while I_N
depends on $R_N{}^2$ in the same way.

Thus

$$\frac{I_N}{I} = \frac{1}{N^2} \cdot \frac{\sin^2 N\gamma}{\sin^2 \gamma} \cdot \frac{\sin^2 \beta}{\beta^2} \quad \cdots \cdots \quad 3.3$$

The results 3.1 and 3.2 are the special forms of this relation when N
has the values 1 and 2. This result is similar to that deduced for two
slits, except that the term $\left(\dfrac{1}{N^2} \cdot \dfrac{\sin^2 N\gamma}{\sin^2 \gamma} \right)$ appears instead of $\cos^2 \gamma$.
It is therefore of interest to consider the form of this term alone;
bearing in mind that the pattern is modulated in reality by the $\dfrac{\sin^2 \beta}{\beta^2}$

term, which represents the intensity distribution over the various directions because of the similar diffraction characteristics of all the separate slits. When γ is a multiple of π the term $\left(\dfrac{1}{N^2} \cdot \dfrac{\sin^2 N\gamma}{\sin^2 \gamma}\right)$ has its largest value, equal to unity. Thus the expression $(a + b) \sin \theta = m\lambda$ again indicates the directions in which these intensity maxima in the interference pattern are found. The forms of $\sin^2 N\gamma$ and of $\sin^2 \gamma$ appear separately, plotted on the same scale, in Fig. 3K (i) and (ii) and the form of $\dfrac{1}{N^2} \dfrac{\sin^2 N\gamma}{\sin_2 \gamma}$ is obtained from the quotient of these, and is shown in Fig. 3K (iii). The value $N = 6$ is used in drawing the curves.

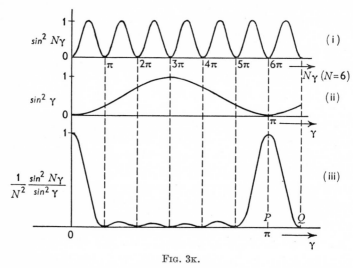

FIG. 3K.

With only two slits a single intensity minimum occurs between any adjacent pair of maxima. When more than two slits are used, provided a and b are unaltered, the directions of the main maxima are unchanged, but $(N - 1)$ minima and $(N - 2)$ subsidiary maxima appear between any adjacent pair of main maxima. The angle between the central direction in any of the main maxima and the direction of the first minimum to either side of it (e.g., the directions corresponding to P and Q in Fig. 3K (iii)) is the *angular half-width* * of that particular maximum, and this is clearly smaller the larger the number N of apertures employed. A further effect of increasing N is to reduce the intensities

---

* When the intensity does not fall to zero on either side of the directions of maximum intensity the half-width may be defined rather differently (as it is defined, for example, for Fabry–Pérot transmission fringes on p. 80).

of the subsidiary maxima relative to the main maxima. The main feature of the action of plane diffraction gratings is now clear in a qualitative way; namely, that the light of any single wavelength is almost entirely concentrated within narrow angular limits about the directions of maximum intensity in the various orders.

The remarks regarding the differing intensities of the principal maxima, which were made in the discussion on the pattern formed by two slits, apply equally when N slits are used. The curve of Fig. 3K (iii) is modulated by the $\sin^2 \beta/\beta^2$ term, and, as before, if $\left(\dfrac{a+b}{a}\right)$ is an integer this order and multiples of it are missing from the pattern.

Angular half-width of intensity maxima. On consideration of Fig. 3K it is evident that whereas the mth order maximum occurs in some direction θ such that $\gamma = m\pi$, the first minima to the sides of this maximum are in the directions $(\theta + \Delta\theta)$ and $(\theta - \Delta\theta)$ such that $N\gamma = (Nm \pm 1)\pi$. If the symbol P_θ is used for the path difference in the direction θ between waves originating at the extreme end apertures of the system, in a case where N is large this is closely equal to N times the path difference in this direction between waves from similar parts of consecutive slits. The above statements concerning the directions θ and $(\theta \pm \Delta\theta)$ may then, by substitution for γ, be written

$$P_\theta = N(a+b) \sin \theta = Nm\lambda$$
$$P_{\theta \pm \Delta\theta} = N(a+b) \sin (\theta \pm \Delta\theta) = (Nm \pm 1)\lambda$$
$$\text{and} \qquad \Delta P = (P_{\theta \pm \Delta\theta} \sim P_\theta) = \pm \lambda$$

Thus the direction of zero intensity immediately to the side of a principal maximum is such that P in this direction is just one wavelength different from its value in the principal maximum direction. Differentiation of the first of the above expressions, at the same time putting $\Delta P = \lambda$, gives

$$\lambda = N(a+b) \cos \theta \,.\, \Delta\theta$$

or
$$\Delta\theta = \frac{\lambda}{N(a+b) \cos \theta} \qquad \cdot \quad \cdot \quad \cdot \quad \cdot \quad \cdot \quad \textbf{3.4}$$

This expression shows clearly the inverse relation between the angular half-width of the principal maximum in the direction θ and the number of apertures N.

Some further clarification will now be made of the physical reasons underlying the fact that the angular half-width corresponds to a change in P of one wavelength λ.

A plane grating having a large number of apertures is considered. Its breadth, transverse to the apertures, is then closely equal to

$N(a + b)$. Thus P, in a general direction ϕ to the undeviated direction, is

$$P_\phi = N(a + b) \sin \phi$$

Let the number of grating intervals between any two apertures be fN, so that f is the fractional ratio between their separation and the full grating breadth, and may have any value (for which fN is integral) ranging between 0 and 1 according to the pair of apertures selected. In the direction ϕ, the path difference between the waves from these apertures is $fN(a + b) \sin \phi$, or fP_ϕ.

The direction $\phi_1 = \theta$, i.e., the direction of the mth principal maximum, will be considered first. Afterwards the directions ϕ_2, ϕ_3, and ϕ_4, progressively different from θ by small amounts, so that ΔP (the difference between P_ϕ and P_θ) has the respective magnitudes $\dfrac{\lambda}{2}$, λ, $\dfrac{3\lambda}{2}$ will be considered in turn.

1. The direction $\phi_1 = \theta$: $P_\theta = Nm\lambda = N(a + b) \sin \theta$, and the contributions from all the apertures are in phase in this direction. For any pair of apertures, the waves differ in path by fP_θ, or $fNm\lambda$, which is an integral multiple of the wavelength, since fN is integral.

2. The direction ϕ_2, such that $\Delta P = \dfrac{\lambda}{2}$: The effect of the whole grating may be discussed by considering it to be made up of a large number of pairs of apertures, each pair being symmetrically disposed about the central line of the grating parallel to the rulings. The path difference between the waves in the direction ϕ_2 from any such pair is fP_ϕ, and, since $P_\phi = P_\theta \pm \dfrac{\lambda}{2}$ and fP_θ is an integral number of wavelengths, these waves differ in phase by an amount corresponding to a path difference of $f\dfrac{\lambda}{2}$. For the pair of apertures at the outermost extremities of the grating breadth, $f = 1$, and the waves are exactly out of phase; but f decreases progressively to zero as aperture pairs progressively nearer the centre of the grating are considered, so that the effective path difference becomes a smaller fraction of $\lambda/2$ and the phase difference correspondingly less, approaching zero for the innermost pairs of apertures of this sort. The total amplitude in the direction ϕ_2 is evidently considerably reduced in comparison with that in the direction θ.

3. The direction ϕ_3, such that $\Delta P = \lambda$: It is here most convenient to divide the grating breadth into two. For every aperture in the upper half, a similar aperture exists in the lower half, spaced exactly half the grating breadth from it. The grating is, in fact, being regarded as $\dfrac{N}{2}$ pairs of apertures side by side, the separation of each pair being

$\frac{N}{2}$ $(a + b)$, and the f value for each pair is $\frac{1}{2}$. The waves from such a pair of apertures differ in path by f. ΔP, i.e., $\lambda/2$. They cancel therefore, and this is true of all the pairs of apertures which together form the grating. Thus the intensity is zero in the direction ϕ_3, and this is in fact the direction of the first minimum to the side of the main intensity maximum.

When N is odd, a single aperture always remains when the grating is divided into a number of pairs of apertures, as described under (2) or (3). It is assumed, however, that N is so large that the effect in any direction of the single aperture remaining is negligible compared with the total intensity effects in the main order directions due to the grating.

4. The direction ϕ_4, such that $\Delta P = \frac{3\lambda}{2}$: Dividing the grating breadth into three equal parts, a similar argument to that used under (3) above may be applied to two of the adjacent thirds of the grating breadth. The effect is therefore that of the remaining one-third. Arguments exactly similar to those appearing under (2) above may be applied to this third of the aperture. The resultant will be less than that obtained in case (2), since only a third of the aperture is contributing effectively in this direction. The direction ϕ_4 is within the first subsidiary maximum to the side of the main maximum.

Extension of these considerations is possible in a very obvious way. The discussion under (3) is of most importance, since it makes clear what is actually occurring in the direction of the first minimum near an order in the wavelength λ.

The type of discussion applied to a grating above is applicable also to a single slit. The pattern formed by such a slit has been described earlier in this chapter. With a single slit the only direction in which the waves from all parts are exactly in phase is the forward direction $\theta = 0$. The direction of the first minimum was shown (on p. 38) to correspond with $\beta = \pi$, and is also that direction such that the path difference between waves originating at the extremities of the slit is λ. It is evidently also possible to explain this by dividing the slit breadth into two, and realizing that for every point in one half a similar point exists in the other which will provide waves $\lambda/2$ different in path in this direction, so that the two halves produce disturbances which completely cancel in this direction. The condition for the first zero to the side of a direction in which all the contributions are in phase is that $\Delta P = \lambda$. This has been used above to obtain the expression 3.4, which is of interest and will be discussed further in connection with resolution properties of gratings. The same condition, applied to a single aperture of a definite breadth, is of use in the consideration of the resolution obtainable with a prism.   This also appears in a later chapter.

Fraunhofer diffraction by a circular aperture

This is similar in principle to the single-slit diffraction discussed earlier.   With a circular aperture and an object point lying on its axis, the pattern may be expected to be radially symmetrical about the axis of the aperture.   It is sufficient, therefore, to consider the effects in a plane containing the axis and one diameter of the aperture.   Fig. 3A is applicable again to this case, a in that figure now being the diameter of the aperture under consideration.   A view of the aperture itself, from the direction of its axis, appears in Fig. 3L.   The area of the aperture may be considered as composed of elements (such as WX) lying side by side, their combined breadths making up the vertical diameter shown, which is also the diameter appearing in Fig. 3A.

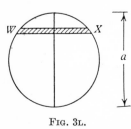

FIG. 3L.

For the slit aperture, the elements of area considered were each of the full length of the slit, their total breadth being a, the breadth of the slit.   As a consequence, the areas of the elements were equal, and their amplitude contributions at some definite distance in the direction θ were all alike. This, together with the fact that the phase of the wave disturbance at J (Fig. 3A) due to any such element varies uniformly with the position of the element within the breadth of the slit, resulted in a phase-amplitude diagram in the form of a circular arc, the resultant being the closing chord.

This is no longer so with the circular aperture, since the lengths, and therefore the areas, of the elements of the aperture (such as WX in Fig. 3K) are not constant.   The elements near the centre of the diameter a, being longer than those towards its extremities, make proportionately larger amplitude contributions.   The phase-amplitude diagram is therefore of the kind suggested by Fig. 3M (i), where each of the amplitude contributions a_1, a_2, a_3 . . . etc., is inclined equally to its nearest neighbours, but those due to the central elements are of larger magnitude than those farther from the centre.   The actual phase-amplitude diagram is the figure towards which Fig. 3M (i) tends when the elements are infinitesimal in breadth and very large in number.   This is a smooth curve having shorter radius of curvature towards its extremities, as indicated in Fig. 3M (ii).   As with a single slit, the figure is more curved the higher the value of θ, the angle between the tangents at its extremities being $\dfrac{2\pi}{\lambda} a \sin \theta$, (or 2β), the phase difference across the full aperture breadth. Unlike the case of the single slit, however, the resultant amplitude is not zero when $\beta = \pi$. Fig. 3M (iii) illustrates this, the tangents at the extremities of the curve being parallel in this figure. The closing chord is not now of zero length, as when the curve is circular in form. Fig. 3M (iv) is the phase-amplitude diagram for the rather larger value of β, for which the ends of the curve just meet, the resultant amplitude then being of zero magnitude.

Full consideration of the mathematics of this curve, deducing its

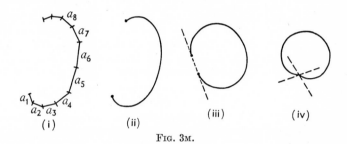

FIG. 3M.

shape using the geometry of Fig. 3L, leads to the conclusion that when the curve closes up the difference in the slopes at the two ends is 2.44π.

Thus,
$$\frac{2\pi}{\lambda} a \sin \theta = 2 \cdot 44\pi$$

or
$$\sin \theta = \frac{1 \cdot 22\lambda}{a} \qquad . \quad . \quad . \quad . \quad 3.5$$

The angular radius θ of the first minimum around the central maximum direction ($\theta = 0$) is given by the above expression. The original method of deduction of this expression, used by Airy, is indicated above. Other mathematical methods lead to the same result. This argument clearly cannot be extended from a point source to a transverse line source, as was possible with a single-slit aperture.

CHAPTER 4

FRESNEL AND OTHER DIFFRACTION EFFECTS

THE considerations of Chapter 2 have shown in a qualitative way that when an aperture is interposed in a convergent or divergent beam of light, a screen behind the aperture receives a patch of light corresponding roughly in shape to that of the transparent parts of the aperture. An exception to this is the case when the effects are viewed in a transverse plane near the point at which the beam focuses; a Fraunhofer diffraction pattern is then seen, the form of which depends on the shape of the aperture but does not correspond to it in appearance. Some important instances of Fraunhofer diffraction have been discussed in Chapter 3. Examples of Fresnel diffraction, and the way in which they are explained, will now be given. These are effects near the edges of shadows of obstacles or apertures occurring in planes so far from the image plane of the system that the general appearance of the shadow is usually recognizably similar to the object producing it. This type of effect merges into the other as the plane on which it is cast is taken nearer to the image plane.

Fresnel diffraction effects are of less general importance than those of the Fraunhofer type, and a few examples only are mentioned here. The examples cited illustrate the main methods of accounting for phenomena of this kind, e.g., *Fresnel's method of zones*, and the use of the *Cornu spiral*. An important outcome of the Fresnel treatment is the justification for Huygens' construction which it supplies, which has been indicated in Chapter 2. The basis of this will now be considered more adequately. Some critical remarks are also necessary at this stage on the Fresnel theory of diffraction, pointing out its shortcomings with an indication of the way in which later theories improve upon it, and the extent to which they themselves are adequate. Finally, this chapter includes a discussion of Babinet's principle, and of the kind of diffraction effects to which it may be applied.

Fresnel's method of zones

Let S, in Fig. 4A, be a source of light and PQ a wave-front from S having radius r. It is first necessary to realize that, since the intensity is proportional to the square of the amplitude of the wave motion, and is also inversely related to the square of the distance from the source, the amplitude at any distance d from a source is proportional to the reciprocal of d. It is convenient to postulate unit amplitude at unit distance from S. The amplitude everywhere in the surface PQ is therefore $1/r$. The zone method of consideration of the effect of the wave-front, at any point C beyond it, consists in dividing the wave-front into imaginary annular zones about the pole of the wave R, i.e., the point where the line CS cuts the wave-front. If x_0 is the distance CR, the zones are such that the distance x from the outer circumference of any zone to C is greater than x_0 by an integral multiple of $\frac{\lambda}{2}$. Thus, for the central zone $x_1 = x_0 + \frac{\lambda}{2}$, for the second zone $x_2 = x_0 + \lambda$, and, generally, $x_m = x_0 + m\frac{\lambda}{2}$. The sizes of the zones depend on the nearest distance x_0 from the wave-front to the point C under consideration, and also on the curvature of the wave-front, i.e., on the distance r. The

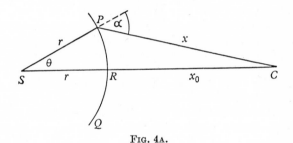

FIG. 4A.

outer zones decrease rapidly in breadth. For the case in which both x_0 and r are one metre, for example, the approximate mean radii of the 5th and 50th zones are 1 mm. and 4 mm. Their breadths are about 0.1 mm. and 0.04 mm.

Consider now a small annular element of area in the wave-front PQ, every point on this area being distant x from C. Let θ be the angle subtended at S by the radius of the annulus, while the angle $d\theta$ is subtended at S by its breadth. The area of such an element is

$$dA = 2\pi r^2 \sin\theta \,.\, d\theta$$

From the triangle PSC (Fig. 4A).

$$x^2 = r^2 + (r + x_0)^2 - 2r(r + x_0)\cos\theta$$

and, by differentiation,

$$x \,.\, dx = r(r + x_0)\sin\theta \,.\, d\theta$$

Thus,
$$dA = \frac{2\pi rx}{(r + x_0)} \,.\, dx$$

Integrating between any two values of x

$$\Delta A = \frac{2\pi r x'}{(r + x_0)} \cdot \Delta x \qquad \ldots \ldots \quad \textbf{4.1}$$

where x' in this expression is the mean of the two values of x concerned. For the mth zone, of area ΔA_m, $x' = \frac{1}{2}(x_m + x_{m-1})$ and $\Delta x = \lambda/2$, and this expression may be written

$$\Delta A_m = \frac{\pi r x' \lambda}{(r + x_0)} \qquad \ldots \ldots \ldots \quad \textbf{4.2}$$

Either of the latter expressions shows that $\dfrac{\Delta A}{x'}$, is constant for annular areas such that Δx is constant. Since the amplitude contribution at C from a narrow annular area depends directly on ΔA and inversely on x', the effects of the differing areas and distances from C just compensate, so that any variation in magnitude of the amplitude contributions at C from these zones must be due to other causes. The inclination to the wave-normal of the direction to C from any zone (e.g., the angle α in Fig. 4A) is a further factor which may affect the magnitude of the contribution at C. Fresnel assumed that the amplitude contributions due to any area were of maximum magnitude in the wave-normal direction, falling off to smaller values at larger inclinations (α) to this direction. It was not necessary to specify the precise manner in which this *inclination factor*, as it was termed, is dependent on the angle α.

It is now possible to consider the form of the phase-amplitude diagram, from which the resultant amplitude at C due to such a system of zones may be found. Considering first the effect of any one zone, it is clear that, since $\Delta x = \lambda/2$, a phase difference of π must exist between the disturbances at C from its innermost and outermost boundaries. If all the elemental annular areas which together make up the zone contributed amplitudes at C which were exactly equal, it is clear from the considerations of the last chapter that the phase-amplitude diagram for the zone would be a circular arc; in this case a semicircle, since the angle between the tangents at its ends must be π. Since, however, the directions to C from the outer parts of such a zone are rather more inclined to the wave-normals than those from the inner parts, Fresnel's postulate regarding the inclination factor means that the actual phase-amplitude diagram has curvature increasing slightly along its length towards the end corresponding to the outer extremity of the zone. The phase-amplitude diagram for the first zone is suggested by the full line OD of Fig. 4B (i), the dotted line being the semicircle having the same radius as OD at the point O. The point O corresponds to R in Fig. 4A, which is the centre of the whole system of zones. Fig. 4B (ii) shows the effect of adding similar curves corresponding to all the other zones, the whole diagram being a spiral-shaped figure, and the closing side the line OE as shown. Since λ is so small, the zones are narrow and the inclination of the directions to C (Fig. 4A) changes very little across any zone. The curvature change along the arc OD is therefore very gradual; more so than can conveniently be indicated in the figure. The effect of a very large number of zones (frequently thousands) needs to be considered before the point E, at the centre of the figure, is reached. It is evident that the resultant amplitude at C, i.e., the length OE in Fig. 4B (ii), is just half that which would be contributed there by the first zone acting alone (i.e., OD). This result may easily be proved by a more mathematical approach, the resultant being the sum of a series of terms due to the separate zones, these terms being alternately positive and negative. The sum

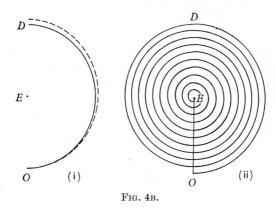

FIG. 4B.

converges towards the above-mentioned limit, the higher terms being progressively smaller in magnitude owing to the introduction of the inclination factor.

This method of division of the wave-front into zones (often called *half-period zones* because of the phase difference of π between the resultants from separate consecutive zones) makes possible a discussion on the basis of rectilinear propagation in normal circumstances, and departures from it near the edges of shadows of obstacles. It is also possible to discuss by its means some aspects of diffraction patterns due to circular apertures and obstacles. These matters will be considered briefly in turn.

Basis of validity of Huygens' principle

The system of half-period zones in the wave-front surrounding the point R (in Fig. 4A) is shown in Fig. 4C. The line FG represents the

C

edge of some obstacle placed so as to obstruct part of the wave-front. The obstacle will first be imagined to be opaque to the left of the line FG so that the portions of the zones lying in this region no longer contribute to the resultant amplitude at C (in Fig. 4A). For example, the length MN of the zone marked k is obscured. If, as is shown in the figure, the edge of the obstacle does not pass near the central zones, the resultant at the field point C is unaffected by the introduction of the obstacle. This is because the inner zones are not impeded and the first several turns of the phase-amplitude diagram, which correspond to them, are exactly as in the case where the wave-front is not obstructed (i.e., as in Fig. 4B (ii)); farther out, when portions of the zones,

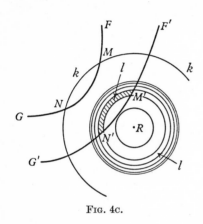

FIG. 4c.

such as MN, are cut out, these portions change in length progressively from zero for the innermost zone affected, and the diagram simply spirals more quickly towards the same end point E. The portion of the spiral contributed by the unobstructed part of the zone k, for instance, is still a near-semicircle (since π is the phase change at C due to the $\lambda/2$ path difference to C across its breadth), but this semicircular arc is shorter, and therefore more curved, than in the unobstructed case, since the whole area of the zone is not contributing. The illumination at C, then, is unaffected by the presence of the obstacle under these conditions.

The case in which C is well inside the geometrical shadow of the obstacle is next discussed. Let FG (Fig. 4c) be the edge of an obstacle, the opaque part of which is now to the right. The transmitted region of the typical zone k is now the length MN. Over the zones for which any part is transmitted this length increases from zero for the zones of smaller radius concerned, and for the larger radii zones may either decrease again (if the line defining the aperture is a closed figure) or increase continuously. The effect at C due to the zones of very large radius is, however, negligible, so that the amplitude contributions at C, which are of opposite sign from alternate zones, increase in magnitude at first from zero and later decrease to zero again as zones of larger radii are considered. It is evident that the sum of such contributions is zero. The illumination well within the shadow is thus zero.

When the obstacle is so placed that the point in the field under consideration (C in Fig. 4A) is near the geometrical shadow edge, the effects obtained are more complicated. The edge of the obstacle then passes through the system of zones quite near to its centre R. Fig. 4c may again be used to discuss this case if the line $F'G'$ is now considered as the edge of the obstacle. An obstacle opaque to the left of the line $F'G'$ is imagined (i.e., C in Fig. 4A is slightly outside the geometrical shadow), but a similar argument applies to the other case. The aperture now obstructs parts of zones quite near the central one, e.g., the shaded area $M'N'$ of the zone marked l is obscured. The zones near the centre have a breadth which is appreciable relative to their circumference. (See, for example, the figures quoted on p. 55 for the sizes of the 5th and 50th zones for a particular case.) As a result of this the elemental annuli which together form any one zone do not generally have the same proportion of their length cut out by the obstacle. For the zone l in Fig. 4c, for example, the fraction of circumference obscured is larger for the outer annuli than for the inner annuli. The effect of this is to change the form of the portion of the phase-amplitude diagram corresponding to this zone. Instead of being semicircular, it is now of some distorted shape, depending on the way the aperture edge cuts the zone across its breadth. This distortion is pronounced only when the zones concerned have appreciable breadth in comparison with their circumference, i.e., for central zones; it has therefore been neglected in the discussion of cases in which the aperture boundary crosses more remote zones from the centre only. It is evident that when early turns of the spiral-shaped phase-amplitude diagram are appreciably distorted, the final resultant amplitude can be changed considerably from the value OE (Fig. 4B) occurring when the wave-front is not impeded.

The statement made in Chapter 2, p. 21 (by use of which it was made evident that Huygens' construction was justified over all parts of wave-fronts except those near their limiting boundaries) is now shown to be reasonable. Provided the obstacle does not obstruct a small area near R, the effect is just as if no obstacle were present. If the whole of this small area is obstructed no light reaches the field-point. Non-rectilinear propagation effects occur only when the edge of the obstacle passes through this small area. The magnitude of the resultant is not immediately predictable at points in this region, but may be expected to vary considerably in this vicinity, i.e., a diffraction pattern may be expected. The vital area near R contains those zones having breadths which are not negligible compared with their circumferences. In all cases of Fresnel diffraction the linear dimensions of this area are very small compared with the longitudinal distances of the arrangement (e.g., the distances r and x_0 in Fig. 4A).

It is evident that the remarks above may need modification in the special case of an aperture or obstacle which is circular with its centre at R, since the system of zones may then be cut off abruptly at the boundary of one of the zones.   Cases of this kind are discussed in the next section.

Fresnel diffraction effects due to circular apertures and obstacles

Fresnel diffraction effects on the axis of circular apertures or obstacles are predictable with ease with the aid of the Fresnel zone picture for the wave-front, and the associated phase-amplitude diagram, or the equivalent mathematical treatment.   Fig. 4D, for instance, shows a phase-amplitude diagram similar to Fig. 4B (ii), but which ceases at a definite point W during its fifth half-revolution.   As mentioned previously, it is convenient to exaggerate the increase in curvature of the spiral along its length in order to obtain better clarity in the figure. The resultant OW corresponds to the amplitude at some point C on the axis of a circular aperture which has such a size that it transmits between four and five of the zones in the wave-front

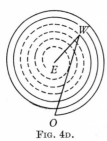

FIG. 4D.

relative to the point C.   As the figure is drawn, the aperture transmits about three-quarters of the breadth of the fifth zone and all the more central zones.   Alteration of the aperture radius without moving the point C would correspond to moving W along the spiral (e.g., along the broken line, if the aperture radius were increased).   The consequent changes in the amplitude OW are clear from the figure.

If a circular obstacle is used instead of an aperture, only the zones outside it are transmitted, so that the portion of the spiral represented by the broken line in Fig. 4D is the phase-amplitude diagram in such a case, and WE is the resultant amplitude.   If a large number of zones is obscured, W is very near to E and the resultant amplitude is practically zero.   If a small circular obstacle is used, which obscures only a few central zones, WE can be quite appreciable. This is the well-known case of illumination on the axis in the (geometrical) shadow of a small circular obstacle.

It should be noted that the two amplitudes OW and WE give OE by vectorial addition.   This is as might be expected, as the apertures in the two cases together constitute an unrestricted aperture, since they are complementary, and OE is the resultant for an unrestricted wave-front.

As the field-point C is moved along the axis of a circular aperture, for example, the size of the zone system around R changes, and so the number of zones transmitted by the aperture varies progressively with consequent alternations in the amplitude and intensity at the point concerned.   It is possible to explain the observed effects by detailed application of these principles.

Zone plates are complex circular diffracting apertures, consisting of alternate transparent and opaque annular zones which correspond exactly with the Fresnel zones for a particular point on the axis of the arrangement. Since consecutive Fresnel zones contribute resultant amplitudes of opposite sign, the amplitudes due to the areas transmitted by such an aperture are all additive. A strong focusing effect therefore occurs at the point on the axis concerned.

The Fresnel zone method loses its simplicity when effects off the axis of a circular aperture are to be explained. The centre R of the zone system no longer coincides with the centre of the aperture, and the amplitudes due to a number of transmitted portions of zones, such as are indicated in Fig. 4E, must be integrated. Methods of performing such calculations have been developed, notably by Lommel, and the experimentally obtained patterns agree with those predicted by these methods. The forms of such patterns in planes near but not quite coincident with the plane into which a point object is being focused are of considerable importance. The Fresnel pattern gradually changes into the Fraunhofer pattern (i.e., the pattern described by equation 3.5) as the image plane is approached; and it is important to know within what limits the pattern resembles that formed in the ideal image plane so closely that the image may still be considered optically perfect. Further discussion on the *Rayleigh limit*, and the tolerances in optical systems which correspond to it, appears in Chapter 6.

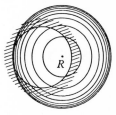

Fig. 4E.

The Cornu spiral and Fresnel integrals

Effects near the edges of shadows of obstacles or apertures having one or more straight edges may be explained by dividing the wave-front in a somewhat different manner from that already described.

Fig. 4F is similar to Fig. 4A, but PQ is now the particular section of the wave-front from S cut by the plane through S and perpendicular to the straight edge X of the obstacle. C again represents the point in the field at which the intensity is to be found; x_0 is its distance from R, the nearest point on the wave-front. The points Y and Z represent the limits in the plane of the figure of the mth area away from R into which the wave-front is divided. These are $x_0 + \dfrac{m\lambda}{2}$ and $x_0 + (m-1)\dfrac{\lambda}{2}$ from C. The mth Fresnel zone is obtained by rotating YR and ZR about R. To discuss the effects of straight edges, however, the wave-front is divided instead into areas limited by semicircles on its surface perpendicular to the plane of the figure at points such as Y and Z. The semicircles drawn in this way through Y and Z have common end points vertically above and below the plane of the figure at S, and Y and Z are their mid-points. The area between them (sometimes referred to as a *lune*) contributes a resultant amplitude at C, which must be the vectorial sum of the amplitudes from all the elemental areas of similar shape which, side by side, make up this area. It may be shown that the amplitude at C due to any one of these elemental areas (e.g., the one passing through Fig. 4F at Y, the uppermost extremity of the lune which has the breadth ZY in the plane of the figure) is the same * as would be contributed by a fixed fraction of the sources in its entire area concentrated at its central point (i.e., at Y in the case cited). It is possible, therefore, to reduce the problem to a two-dimensional one, the effect at C due to the mth

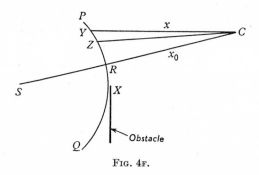

FIG. 4F.

lune being that of a uniform distribution of coherent sources along the line YZ. A uniform distribution of sources over the whole line PQ will produce the effect of the whole unobstructed wave-front at C. The phase-amplitude diagram corresponding to this arrangement of sources will now be considered.

Let dl be an element of the line PQ, at distance l from R and x from C. It proves to be necessary to consider only values of l quite small relative to SR (i.e., r) and x_0 (Fig. 4F); and it is adequate to assume that the slightly differing values of x for the various elements of PQ concerned cause no appreciable change in their amplitude contributions at C. Also the inclination factor may be neglected in these circumstances. The phase of the contribution at C from the element dl differs from that at the same instant from the central element at R by an amount α equal to $\frac{2\pi}{\lambda}(x - x_0)$. It may be shown geometrically that, within the limits

---

* In magnitude. There is a 45° phase difference which is unimportant for the present argument.

mentioned above, the quantity $\dfrac{l^2(r + x_0)}{2rx_0}$ may be substituted for $(x - x_0)$.

Thus
$$\alpha = \frac{\pi l^2(r + x_0)}{\lambda r x_0}$$

This equation shows that α depends on the square of l. A uniform distribution of sources along PQ is being considered, and the effects on the amplitude due to varying distance and direction to C from different points on the line are assumed negligible. It is evident therefore that any length v of the curved phase-amplitude diagram is directly proportional to the length l of PQ to which it corresponds. The phase-

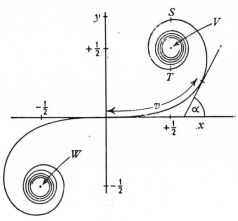

FIG. 4G.

amplitude diagram is thus of a form such that its gradient α is related to its length v from the origin by the expression

$$\alpha = \text{constant} \times v^2$$

The magnitude of the constant merely affects the scale of the figure. The figure is called a *Cornu spiral* and the equation

$$\alpha = \frac{\pi}{2} v^2 \qquad . \quad . \quad . \quad . \quad . \quad . \quad \textbf{4.3}$$

is usually quoted for this type of curve. Fig. 4G shows the form and scale of this latter curve. The two spiral-shaped portions represent the effects of the portions of the wave-front above and below the point R in Fig. 4F. The slope of the curve changes by π across each lune, e.g., the first and second lunes above R correspond to the portions OS and ST of the curve (where O is the origin).

The full curve corresponds to the unrestricted wave-front, and the resultant in this case is the line joining the points V and W, which are the points towards which the curve gradually spirals at its ends. These points are effectively reached after quite a small number of turns of the spiral-shaped portions of the curve. Thus the consideration of a limited number of lunes, to either side of the point R, is always sufficient. This justifies the use of the approximation that l is much smaller than r and x_0 in the deduction of the shape of the phase-amplitude diagram.

When the wave-front is limited by two parallel straight edges, with an aperture between them, only a portion of the full Cornu spiral corresponds to the transmitted wave-front. If (x_1, y_1) and (x_2, y_2) are the co-ordinates of the points on the curve corresponding to the aperture edges, the resultant amplitude is the straight line joining these points. The intensity depends on the square of this, i.e., upon

$$(x_1 - x_2)^2 + (y_1 - y_2)^2 \quad . \quad . \quad . \quad . \quad \textbf{4.4}$$

The case of a single straight edge is simply the case in which the second edge is considered a large distance removed in the transverse direction so that (x_2, y_2) is then at one of the end-points of the curve (V or W). The components in the x and y co-ordinate directions of an element dv of the length of the Cornu spiral are

$$dx = dv \cos \alpha \quad \text{and} \quad dy = dv \sin \alpha$$

Hence, by integration,

$$x_1 - x_2 = \int_{v_2}^{v_1} \cos \frac{\pi v^2}{2} \, . \, dv$$

and

$$y_1 - y_2 = \int_{v_2}^{v_1} \sin \frac{\pi v^2}{2} \, . \, dv$$

where v_1 and v_2 are the lengths along the curve from the origin to the points (x_1, y_1) and (x_2, y_2); v_1 and v_2 are directly related to the corresponding transverse distances from the pole of the wave-front (R in Fig. 4F) to the obstacle edges. The intensity at the point concerned is therefore proportional to

$$\left[\int_{v_2}^{v_1} \cos \frac{\pi v^2}{2} \, . \, dv \right]^2 + \left[\int_{v_2}^{v_1} \sin \frac{\pi v^2}{2} \, . \, dv \right]^2 . \quad . \quad . \quad \textbf{4.5}$$

The x and y co-ordinates of any point on the Cornu spiral are

$$\int_0^v \cos \frac{\pi v^2}{2} \, . \, dv \quad \text{and} \quad \int_0^v \sin \frac{\pi v^2}{2} \, . \, dv$$

These are known as the *Fresnel integrals*, often denoted by C and S respectively.

Fresnel obtained the expression 4.5 by a more direct mathematical approach to the problem. The idea of plotting the Fresnel integrals on a system of rectangular axes, and interpreting straight-edge diffraction effects by means of the curve so obtained, was introduced later by Cornu. It will be evident in the next section that the use of the Cornu spiral enables the nature of the expected phenomena in particular cases to be visualized easily and without detailed mathematical treatment. If in any case the full details of the diffraction pattern are required, however, the form of the spiral must be known accurately. Since this involves a knowledge of the Fresnel integrals, the full quantitative solution is mathematically equivalent to the original Fresnel solution of the problem. Generally, it may be said that the graphical (or phase-amplitude diagram) method of approach to any diffraction problem possesses the above-mentioned advantage as compared with more purely mathematical methods, though the methods are not essentially different in their explanation of the full details of the patterns obtained. The introduction of graphical methods is mainly attributable to Cornu.

Straight-edge diffraction effects

A single example is chosen to illustrate the explanation of straight-edge diffraction effects by means of the Cornu spiral. This is the case of the single straight edge.

Consider the effect of moving the point C in Fig. 4F steadily downwards so that it passes through the edge of the shadow of the obstacle X. In doing this R moves progressively down PQ from a point well above to a point well below X. At the commencement of this motion the whole of the Cornu spiral must be considered, giving the resultant VW at C. As R approaches X, however, a significant part of the half of the wave-front below R is cut off at the obstacle. The left hand half of the spiral, which corresponds to the part of the wave-front below R, is therefore only partly complete, as far as the point Q, as shown in Fig. 4H (i). The length OQ along the curve depends on the length RX, which is not obscured. When C is on the line SX (Fig. 4F), i.e., on the geometrical shadow edge, the whole of the wave-front below R is obscured and Q in Fig. 4H (i) is at O. As R goes below X, Q passes from O along the spiral towards V and the resultant VQ diminishes progressively. Fig. 4H (ii) shows the form of the resultant amplitude variation with the position of the point R relative to X. The amplitude VO when C is exactly on the geometrical shadow edge has exactly half the value VW which is obtained when C is well outside the shadow. The intensity variation follows a similar form to Fig. 4H (ii), depending on the square of the amplitude.

The reader should have no difficulty in using the Cornu spiral to explain other cases. When two near straight edges are used (with an aperture between them) the curve is incomplete at both ends, to different extents in different positions in the field, and the resultant is the straight line joining its two end points. When a narrow obstacle is

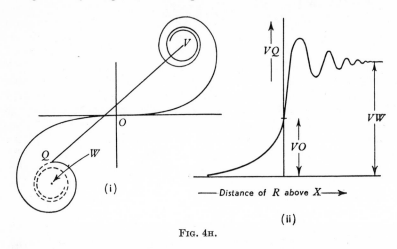

FIG. 4H.

used, a central part of the curve is cut out, and the amplitude is obtained by vectorial addition of the straight lines which close the two end portions.

Critical remarks on Fresnel diffraction theory

Essentially, the explanation of diffraction phenomena which has been outlined in the previous pages is that introduced by Fresnel. All parts of a wave-front are considered as sources of secondary waves, and the effect at a later time is the result of superposition of these secondary waves. Assuming in addition that obstacles simply stop those parts of wave-fronts falling upon them, without affecting the remaining parts, and introducing also the inclination factor, practically all intensity patterns obtained in normal diffraction experiments may be explained. While the theory is adequate for the prediction of the patterns expected, it is deficient in some other respects. The inclination factor appears simply as an additional assumption necessary to give the correct results; also the phase of the resultant displacement at a point, predicted by the Fresnel theory, is incorrect by $\pi/2$. (Referring to Fig. 4B (ii), for instance, there is evidently a difference in phase of $\pi/2$ between the resultant OE and the contribution from the pole of the wave which has the phase corresponding to the direction of the tangent at O.) The secondary waves must be considered as starting with a phase $\pi/2$ in advance of that actually existing over the wave-front if the correct phase (as well as amplitude) is to be obtained by superposition of these waves at points beyond the wave-front.

A more fundamental approach to the subject, due to Kirchhoff (1883), based on the general differential equation for wave motion, corrects for these last-mentioned deficiencies. By a similar but less comprehensive approach, Stokes showed in 1849 that the magnitude of the inclination factor, in any direction α to the wave-normal in the forward direction, is $\left(\dfrac{1 + \cos \alpha}{2}\right)$. This evidently has the necessary values of unity near the forward wave-normal and zero in the reverse direction. This is a special deduction from a more general expression for the inclination factor in the Kirchhoff theory. The law of addition of the effects of small elements of a wave-front, assumed by the Fresnel theory, is given a basic mathematical justification by the Kirchhoff theory; and the inclination factor is no longer a separate arbitrary postulate, but is shown also to be a consequence of the wave equation.

Experiments performed by Gouy (reference 22) have demonstrated the existence of a *phase jump* of magnitude π as light passes through and beyond a focus. Half of this phase change may be considered as occurring progressively as the light nears the focus, and the remainder after the focus has been passed. As light passes out from a small source, a progressive phase change of $\pi/2$ may thus be expected to occur within short distances of the source. A similar effect is expected theoretically with the longer electro-magnetic waves from a simple Hertzian dipole oscillator, the phase change taking place within distances of the order of wavelengths from the source. These considerations afford some justification for the adjustment of phase by $\pi/2$, which must be applied in a somewhat arbitrary way to all the secondary sources in a wave-front, if the Fresnel theory is to give the correct phase at all points in the field. Since the phase variation near a focus is inherent in the wave equation, the Kirchhoff theory, which is based only on this equation, accounts correctly for the phases at points in the field.

The assumption that the parts of a wave-front passed by an aperture are completely unaffected right up to the very edges of the aperture is known as *St. Venant's hypothesis*. This is a basic assumption common to the Fresnel and Kirchhoff theories, but is not strictly valid. The aperture edges may be expected to affect the parts of wave-fronts passing within distances of the order of wavelengths from them, in a manner depending on the form and material of the diffracting edge and the electromagnetic nature of the light waves. The consequence of ignoring these effects is that the predictions of the theories are not reliable at large angles of diffraction, nor very close to the diffracting apertures. The circumstances in which the theories are not applicable are outside the range of normal optical diffraction experiments.

References to accounts of the development of theories of diffraction appear in the bibliography (e.g. references 6, 12, 18).

Babinet's principle

Two diffracting screens A and B such that the apertures of one screen exactly correspond to the opaque parts of the other are said to be complementary screens. Babinet's principle states that, in certain circumstances, when either of two such screens is interposed at the same place in an otherwise unrestricted beam of light, the intensity patterns obtained are similar.

It is clear that, if St. Venant's hypothesis is accepted, the portions of a wave-front transmitted by screen A and those transmitted by B (when it is substituted for A) together constitute the full unrestricted wave-front. At any point which is not illuminated when no diffraction

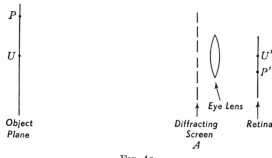

Fig. 4J.

screen is interposed, the resultant amplitude there due to the unimpeded wave-front is zero. The amplitudes there due to the portions transmitted by A and B must therefore be equal and opposite; and thus the intensities due to either A or B, being dependent on the squares of the amplitudes, must be the same. Babinet's principle applies only at points which receive no illumination when no diffracting screen is inserted in the beam of light concerned. It applies therefore to effects occurring in or near transverse planes into which images of small objects are cast, and only in regions of these planes away from the image points themselves, these regions being unilluminated except when diffracting screens are introduced into the beams. The patterns obtained with the screens interposed, being in the image plane of the arrangement, are Fraunhofer diffraction patterns.

A particular case is illustrated diagrammatically in Fig. 4J. Here the eye lens focuses the small object U at U' on the retina. A region near U' will be illuminated due to the combined effect of diffraction at the eye-lens aperture and aberrations of the lens itself. But in the absence of other diffracting screens this region will be of very small dimensions. Points such as P', away from U', will be unilluminated. Inserting now a diffracting screen A, a Fraunhofer pattern forms on the retina, and points such as P' are then illuminated. Whichever of the two complementary screens A or B is used, the patterns away from U' are the same. Since the eye is focused so that the retina is conjugate with the object plane through U, the patterns appear to be in this plane around U.

If the screen A consists of a large number of similar opaque particles of circular section, arranged at random on a transparent mounting, the pattern will be identical (except at its centre) with that due to a similar arrangement of fine circular holes. It may be shown that the pattern due to a random arrangement of similar apertures is the same as that due to one aperture of the same sort but of higher intensity. Hence the pattern obtained is the same as that due to Fraunhofer diffraction at a circular aperture; the first minimum around the centre subtending the angle $\dfrac{1 \cdot 22\lambda}{a}$, where a is the diameter of the particles.

This angle may be measured by adjustment of the distance of the object point U until the first dark ring is of a definite known diameter. This is usually done by having small subsidiary holes, arranged in a circle around the central hole U, in the screen placed in front of the light source. It is then a simple matter to fit the diffraction ring to the circle which is defined in this way. This arrangement for measuring the diameters of small particles is known as *Young's eriometer*. The name is derived from the Greek $\epsilon\rho\iota\text{o}\nu$, meaning " wool "; Young first used the method to examine diffraction patterns formed by wool fibres, and to sort fibres into various grades of fineness.

CHAPTER 5

THE PRODUCTION OF SIMPLE
INTERFERENCE EFFECTS—SOME
APPLICATIONS

THE simple devices for the production of interference fringes described in the first section of this chapter are well known; only a brief outline is therefore given, with a note of special points. The remainder of the chapter is devoted to effects of thin films. A separate chapter is devoted to instruments which depend on the principles outlined here, but some other important applications of thin-film interference effects are included in the present chapter.

Simple double-beam interference arrangements

Young's double slit arrangement consists of an illuminated single slit, the light from which falls on a screen in which are two close slits parallel to the first. Each slit of the pair passes a different portion of any

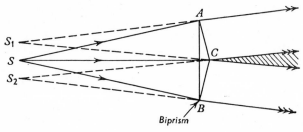

FIG. 5A.

wave-front from the single slit, and the waves from each transmitted portion overlap and interfere in the region beyond the double slit. The fringes may be viewed by an eyepiece focused on any position illuminated by both beams. Alternatively, the eye may be placed just behind the double slit, so that it receives and focuses the emergent beams issuing in the various directions. The arrangement is then essentially that illustrated in Fig. 4J, and a Fraunhofer pattern of the form described by equation 3.2 then appears in the plane of the single object slit.

Fresnel's biprism is a prism of the shape indicated in Fig. 5A, and may be considered as two thin prisms having vertices at A and B and joined base to base.   A line source S, parallel to the edge C, emits light which after deviation appears to originate at S_1 or S_2 according as it has passed through the top or bottom half of the biprism.   Two effective line sources S_1 and S_2 are thus produced, and the beams from the two parts of the biprism produce interference effects which are viewable anywhere where these beams overlap (i.e., in the shaded region of Fig. 5A).

Fresnel's bimirror consists of a pair of plane mirrors arranged so that their normal directions are slightly inclined.   A line source in front of the mirrors, opposite and parallel to their line of junction, produces two images in close proximity; the reflected light beams, which seem to originate at these images, interfere wherever they overlap.

Lloyd's single mirror was described on p. 45.   Diffraction affects the interference patterns in a similar way to that discussed there in all the cases now being outlined.   A feature of the Lloyd mirror fringes is that the image source is effectively out of phase with the real source because of a change of phase of π on reflection.   The optical-path difference to any point in the field is therefore $\lambda/2$ different from the geometrical-path difference.   The intensity is therefore zero wherever the geometrical-path difference is zero or an integral multiple of λ.

Split lens arrangements (due to Billet) produce double images of a single object source by slight relative displacement of the two halves of a lens.   The beams from these images then interfere.   The images of the object may be separated along or across the lens axis by longitudinal or transverse displacement of the two parts of the lens.

Thin-film fringes—localized and non-localized fringes

A thin film of transparent material (for example, a soap film or the air space between two pieces of plate glass) produces from a single incident beam a reflected beam consisting of two * parts, some of the light being reflected at each of its boundaries.   These reflected beams interfere.   Fig. 5B shows how, in the case of a parallel-sided reflecting film, the light emergent in any direction BE is made up of the parts which follow the courses $FACBE$ and GBE.   The resultant amplitude in this direction depends on the difference of phase between these two beams.   This is determined by the optical-path difference, and it will now be shown how this depends on the thickness e of the film and the direction in which the reflected light is viewed.   The paths of the two constituent emergent waves in the direction BE are unequal, since one covers the distance DB in the medium of refractive index n_0,

---

* For the present, effects of multiple reflection within the film are ignored. These are small except when the reflectivities of the surfaces are enhanced, e.g., by silvering.

whereas the other covers AC and CB in the material of refractive index n. The path difference w arising on this account is therefore

$$w = n(AC + CB) - n_0(DB)$$

Now

$$AC = CB = e/\cos \phi$$

$$DB = AB \sin \theta$$

and

$$AB = 2e \tan \phi$$

also,

$$n_0 \sin \theta = n \sin \phi$$

Hence

$$w = 2ne \cos \phi \quad . \quad . \quad . \quad . \quad . \quad . \quad \textbf{5.1}$$

For an air film between glass or other transparent plates, $n = 1$ and the angle of incidence θ within the first glass plate corresponds to incident and emergent angles ϕ in the air above this plate. ϕ in the ex-

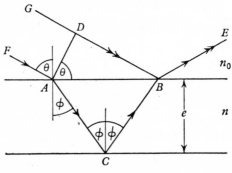

Fig. 5B.

pression 5.1 is then the inclination to the normal of the direction of viewing. With films of other materials $n \neq 1$, and ϕ is the refraction angle within the material corresponding to the direction of viewing θ outside.

A parallel-sided reflecting film and parallel incident light have been assumed in the above deduction. If light is supplied over a range of incident directions the path difference changes with direction, maxima and minima in the reflected light intensity occurring in directions such that the optical-path difference is $m\lambda$ and $(m + \frac{1}{2})\lambda$ respectively, m being any integer. As has been mentioned on p. 71, a phase change of π may take place on reflection at an interface between media; this is found to occur only when the light is incident on the side of the boundary where the refractive index is lower. One only of the two reflecting surfaces is of this type in the cases at present discussed. The optical-path difference, allowing for this phase change, is $\left(w + \dfrac{\lambda}{2}\right)$.

Thus the conditions for cancellation or reinforcement of the reflected waves are:

$$2ne \cos \phi = m\lambda \quad \text{cancellation} \quad . \quad . \quad . \quad . \quad \textbf{5.2a}$$

and $\qquad 2ne \cos \phi = (m + \frac{1}{2})\lambda \text{ reinforcement} \quad . \quad . \quad . \quad \textbf{5.2b}$

The mth order reinforcement occurs in all directions making the constant angle ϕ (given by 5.2b) with the normal, provided light is incident in such a way as to produce reflection in these directions. A converging lens, with its axis in the direction of the normal, may be used to focus the effects into its focal plane. Beams of constant direction to the normal then focus into a ring around the focal point; and the whole fringe pattern consists of a number of alternately bright and dark rings of this kind. Interference fringes of this type, produced by a parallel-sided film, illuminated by convergent (or divergent) light, are termed *fringes of equal inclination*.

When a non-parallel-sided film is considered, the expression 5.1 is no longer precisely accurate, but nevertheless is closely true, provided the change of thickness e is not appreciable, relative to the wavelength, over distances along the film such as AB in Fig. 5B. It may therefore be applied to non-uniform films provided these are thin, and it is clear that the approximation involved in using it is especially closely accurate when the incidence is near the normal direction.

In Fig. 5c, beams from a source S are shown reflected at a thin air-film in the form of a wedge. For clarity the angle of the wedge is exaggerated, and the thickness of the glass plates at its boundaries is reduced to zero. The incident beam from S extends over a wide range of incidence angles, but attention is confined in the figure to those incident directions which produce reflected beams from the top and bottom of the film, *both* of which are accepted by the viewing system (indicated by the lens L, which may be the eye lens or the objective of a microscope). These are evidently the only reflected beams which will be seen to interfere. The angle of the wedge being much smaller in reality than is indicated in the figure, the reflected beams leave the two surfaces from areas almost equidistant from O, and their general directions are only slightly inclined. They overlap therefore over a considerable region, and fringes which are essentially similar to those produced by a Fresnel bi-mirror arrangement may be viewed anywhere in this region. For the production of these fringes a point or line source (parallel to the apex O of the wedge) is necessary. The term *non-localized fringes* is used for this type of interference-fringe system. All the fringes so far discussed in this chapter are of this type. With an air-wedge, however, there is one definite surface within the region of overlap of the reflected beams upon which it is possible to focus the eye or other viewing arrangement and to see fringes even when an extended source of light is used.   This is the surface indicated by the broken line PQ in Fig. 5c.   Any point on this surface (such as T) is the intersection point of two reflected rays, from the upper and lower surfaces of the film, which were originally one and the same incident ray from S.   It may be shown that movement of S over a small range does not affect the position and spacing of the fringes in this surface. Thus an extended source near S will produce sharp fringes in this surface, since the fringes due to all its parts superpose.   Extended sources are normally employed in observing thin-film fringes, and the

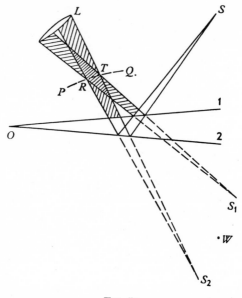

Fig. 5c.

fringes viewed in these circumstances are termed *localized fringes*. Any device which produces localized fringes also produces non-localized fringes when a suitable slit source is employed.   Most arrangements which produce non-localized fringes, except those which are basically of the air-wedge type, do not also produce localized fringes when extended sources are employed.   Because of the nature of these arrangements, the surface in which localized fringes should occur is not in the region actually traversed by both the interfering beams.   For a fuller discussion of localized and non-localized fringes the reader is referred to reference 23.

The surface of localization is the locus of points such as T in Fig. 5c. The section of this surface in the plane of the figure may be shown to be

a semicircle, passing through the apex O of the wedge and having diameter OW, where W lies midway between the two images S_1 and S_2 of
the source.   In practice, in the majority of cases the angle and thickness of the wedge are very small and the distance from O of S (and
of W) is large.   It is therefore a close approximation to replace this
semicircle by its tangent at O.   The surface of localization is then a
plane through the apex of the wedge and perpendicular to the direction
of viewing.   In the special case of viewing in a direction perpendicular
to one of the faces of the wedge the fringes appear in coincidence with
this face.   If the thin film is non-uniform in the sense that the small
angle between the bounding surfaces varies from point to point, the
surface of localization is no longer plane.   It is, however, always in
the vicinity of the film if the fringes are viewed from a perpendicular
direction, and usually within the depth of focus of the viewing device
when the latter is focused on the film.

Multiple-beam thin-film fringes

Interference effects in reflected light from a thin film have so far been
discussed assuming there are only two reflected beams to be considered,
i.e., those returning into the initial medium after single reflections at

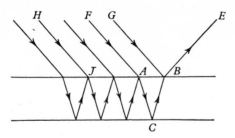

Fig. 5d.

either the first or the second face of the film.   It is evident from Fig.
5D, however, that the reflected light along any direction BE is not only
made up of the parts following the courses GBE and $FACBE$, but there
are other, weaker, contributions which have suffered multiple internal
reflections before emergence.   For example, part of the light incident
along the line HJ ultimately emerges along BE after suffering five
internal reflections,   These contributions may be almost negligible if
the surfaces are of low reflecting power.   The arrangement is then
effectively a double-beam interference arrangement, and many of its
features can be discussed without reference to the other interfering
beams.   This has been done in the previous section.   The effect of
considering also the multiple reflections is discussed further here,

since a number of applications of thin-film interference employ silvered and other high-reflecting surfaces. Consider light waves advancing in some definite direction towards a single surface separating two optical media, as indicated in Fig. 5E (i). Let the amplitudes of the reflected and transmitted portions of the wave system have magnitudes which are fractions r and t of the incident wave amplitude. For convenience consider unit incident amplitude, so that r and t are the actual amplitudes of the reflected and transmitted waves. If the reflected and transmitted waves are reversed, they should together reconstitute the original incident wave travelling in the reverse direction. Let r' and t' be the reflected and transmitted fractions of the amplitudes of waves incident on the surface within the second medium. The two waves of amplitude r and t when reversed should then produce

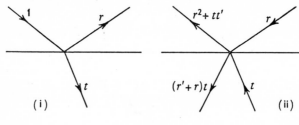

FIG. 5E.

the effect shown in Fig. 5E (ii). This is equivalent simply to the original incident wave of unit amplitude, reversed in direction, if

$$r' = -r \qquad \text{5.3a}$$

and

$$1 - r^2 = tt' \qquad \text{5.3b}$$

The first of these expressions indicates that the reflected amplitude in the case of incidence from one side of the refracting surface is reversed in sign relative to that occurring when the incidence is from the other side. Waves having amplitudes opposite in sign are clearly different in phase by π; this expression is therefore the basis of the introduction of a *change of phase on reflection* of this amount when discussing interference effects of thin films, as on p. 72, for example. It is not, however, apparent from the above treatment (due to Stokes) that the phase change on reflection arises when the light is incident in the medium of lower refractive index and not in the other case. This fact emerges as a result of considerations involving the electro-magnetic nature of light.

Using equation 5.3a, it is now evident that if absorption of light is neglected the amplitudes of the various waves into which a single wave of unit amplitude divides, when incident upon a parallel-sided thin film, are those indicated in Fig. 5F. Absorption of light in the film would result in reduction of the amplitudes below the magnitudes indicated. The reduction would be larger for those waves traversing greater distances within the film, i.e., for the waves suffering more internal reflections. If the film is highly transparent, or alternatively, very thin, the reduction in amplitude due to this cause is inappreciable, and the amplitudes shown in Fig. 5F may be taken as correct.

Consider first the wave systems returning into the first medium, which have amplitudes r, $-rtt'$, $-r^3tt'$, ... etc. As has already been explained (and illustrated in Fig. 5D), the light emerging in any direction consists of waves of all these amplitudes. The path differ-

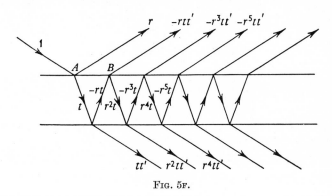

FIG. 5F.

ence between any consecutive pair of these waves is $2ne \cos \phi$, according to equation 5.1, the symbols of Fig. 5B being again employed. The corresponding phase difference, which will be denoted by δ, is $\frac{4\pi}{\lambda} ne \cos \phi$. The resultant amplitude is obtained in the usual way by vectorial addition of all the constituent amplitudes, with due regard to their phases.

When $2ne \cos \phi = m\lambda$ (or $\delta = 2m\pi$) the amplitudes are all in the same straight line in the phase-amplitude diagram, and the resultant R_r is therefore obtained by numerical addition.

Thus
$$R_r = r - rtt' - r^3tt' - r^5tt' - \ldots \text{ etc.}$$
$$= r[1 - tt'(1 + r^2 + r^4 + \ldots)]$$
$$= r\left[1 - \frac{tt'}{1 - r^2}\right]$$
$$= 0 \qquad \text{from equation 5.3b}$$

All the terms after the first in the above expression for R_r are seen to combine to cancel the first.   Complete extinction therefore occurs when the condition 5.2a is satisfied, the light reflected at the first surface being exactly cancelled by the combined effect of all the other beams emerging in the same direction after suffering internal reflections. It is evident that, when r is small, tt' or $(1 - r^2)$ is almost unity, and the r^3tt' and later terms may be neglected.   The extinction may then be considered as caused by the cancellation of the first two reflected beams only.   The above discussion shows, however, that perfect cancellation occurs when 5.2a is satisfied whatever the magnitude of r, absorption being assumed inappreciable.

Consider now the transmitted light, at first confining attention to the case just discussed for reflected light, viz.: $\delta = 2m\pi$.   It is evident that the amplitudes of the various transmitted waves also add numerically in this case.   The resultant transmitted amplitude R_t is thus

$$R_t = tt' + r^2tt' + r^4tt' + \ldots$$

$$= \frac{tt'}{1 - r^2}$$

$$= 1 \qquad\qquad \text{from equation 5.3b}$$

As may be expected, the incident amplitude is entirely transmitted when complete extinction of the reflected light occurs.

The magnitude of r * has therefore no effect on either the intensities

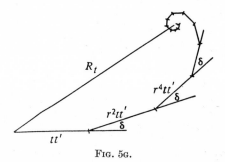

Fig. 5g.

of the maxima in the transmitted light, or on the perfection of the extinctions in the reflected light.   It does, however, affect the sharpness of the transmitted maxima (and, correspondingly, the sharpness of the reflected minima) in an important way.   With higher-reflecting surfaces the number of transmitted beams whose amplitudes are of significant magnitude is larger.   When these beams are not exactly

* The ratio of the reflected intensity to the incident intensity upon a surface is known as the *reflecting power* or *reflection coefficient* of the surface.   This is evidently r^2, since intensity depends on the square of the amplitude.

in phase, i.e., in some direction which is not quite that of any of the transmitted maxima, the resultant is smaller than it would be if fewer beams contributed effectively to the light in this direction. This is a similar effect to that arising with multiple slits, discussed on p. 48, where the effect of increasing the number of beams was shown to be that of sharpening the principal maxima. Fig. 5G shows the phase-amplitude diagram relevant in the present case. The components of R_t in directions parallel and perpendicular to the amplitude tt' of the first emergent wave are clearly

$$tt' + r^2 tt' \cos \delta + r^4 tt' \cos 2\delta + \ldots$$

and $$r^2 tt' \sin \delta + r^4 tt' \sin 2\delta + \ldots$$

The resultant intensity I_t is proportional to $R_t{}^2$, which is the sum of the squares of these components.

Thus

$$I_t \propto [1 + r^2 \cos \delta + r^4 \cos 2\delta + \ldots]^2 \\ + [r^2 \sin \delta + r^4 \sin 2\delta + \ldots]^2$$

This expression may be shown to be equivalent mathematically to

$$I \propto \frac{1}{1 - 2r^2 \cos \delta + r^4} \quad \text{or} \quad \frac{1}{(1 - r^2)^2 + 4r^2 \sin^2 \delta/2}$$

The maxima occur, as required, when $\delta = 2m\pi$, and the expression may be written,

$$\frac{I}{I_{\max.}} = \frac{(1 - r^2)^2}{(1 - r^2)^2 + 4r^2 \sin^2 \delta/2} \quad \cdot \quad \cdot \quad \cdot \quad \cdot \quad \textbf{5.4}$$

The minima in the transmitted intensity occur when $\delta = \pi, 3\pi, 5\pi$, etc., and the minimum intensities are given by

$$\frac{I_{\min.}}{I_{\max.}} = \frac{(1 - r^2)^2}{(1 + r^2)^2} \quad \cdot \quad \cdot \quad \cdot \quad \cdot \quad \cdot \quad \cdot \quad \textbf{5.5}$$

The contrast between the extreme transmitted intensities is evidently enhanced by increase in r. This contrast is often specified numerically by a quantity V, known as the *visibility* of the interference fringes, as follows:

$$V = \frac{I_{\max.} - I_{\min.}}{I_{\max.} + I_{\min.}} = \frac{2r^2}{1 + r^4} \quad \cdot \quad \cdot \quad \quad \textbf{5.6}$$

This evidently increases with the reflection coefficient r^2. Curves showing the form of the transmitted fringes for $r^2 = 0.05$ and $r^2 = 0.30$ are illustrated in Fig. 5H. The reflected light fringes are exactly complementary to the transmitted fringes, provided it is assumed no absorption occurs, and, as already explained, they have minimum intensities of zero magnitude. Reflected intensities, for the same two values of r^2, are also shown in Fig. 5H.

The *half-width* of one of the peaks in the transmitted intensity may be defined as the range of phase values within which the intensity is greater than half the maximum value. Insertion of $\dfrac{I}{I_{\text{max.}}} = \tfrac{1}{2}$ in equation 5.4 leads to the value $4 \sin^{-1}\left(\dfrac{1 - r^2}{2r}\right)$ for this quantity. As with diffraction gratings, if wavelengths of closely equal magnitudes are to be separated by a device such as this, the maxima in any one wavelength must be sharp. The half-width value obtained above decreases with increase of r, so that higher wavelength resolution is obtainable with more highly reflecting surfaces. Further remarks on the Fabry-

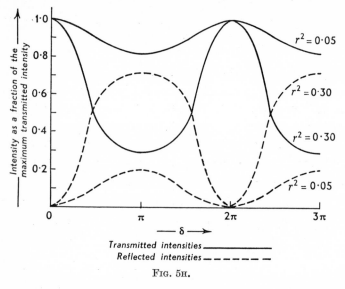

Transmitted intensities ——————
Reflected intensities — — — — — —

Fig. 5h.

Pérot interferometer, which consists essentially of a multiple-beam thin-film arrangement producing fringes of equal inclination, appear in Chapter 8.

It must be emphasized again that since absorption effects have been neglected, effects obtained in practice may not correspond exactly with those which have been deduced (see reference 8). This is especially the case when the reflecting properties of surfaces are enhanced by silver or other deposits which, in the endeavour to obtain high reflection, may no longer be thin enough for the absorption to be inappreciable. More complicated phase changes also arise at the metal surfaces in such cases. The reflected and transmitted fringe systems are no longer complementary, and the maxima in both sets of fringes may occur at the same incidence angles. The general characteristics of the reflected and transmitted interference systems are, however, sufficiently described by the foregoing discussion and its deductions.

Interference fringes known as fringes of superposition, or *Brewster's fringes*, are employed in several interferometric procedures, and a brief discussion of their production may be included here. An arrangement with two parallel optically-flat reflecting surfaces is known as an etalon. If light passes through two such etalons inclined at a small angle α, and if the etalons are of almost equal thickness, or of thicknesses which are almost in a simple numerical ratio, several possibilities exist for the production of beams which may interfere. Fig. 5J shows light incident upon etalons 1 and 2, θ being the angle of incidence upon the first and $(\theta + \alpha)$ upon the second. Consider first the beams represented by b and c, which suffer double reflection at 1 and 2 respectively. Each of these has a longer optical path than the beam passing straight

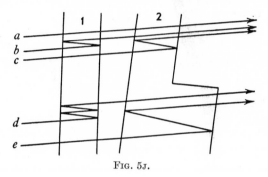

FIG. 5J.

through both etalons (represented by a); b is longer than a by $2e_1 \cos \theta$, and c is longer than a by $2e_2 \cos (\theta + \alpha)$.* It is clear that if α is small and e_1 and e_2 closely equal, the path difference between b and c is small and dependent on θ. A telescope collecting the emergent light will therefore see alternate dark and bright fringes. The case discussed is the simplest one, but several other possibilities exist. The lower half of Fig. 5J shows, as an example, a case in which e_2 is about twice e_1 and the beam d suffering four internal reflections in 1 is of length very closely equal to the beam e which is doubly reflected in 2. White light fringes (see p. 88) of this type may be obtained, the zero-order white fringe being in the direction such that the two interfering light paths are exactly equal.

A further method of displaying Brewster's fringes is to make the two etalons exactly parallel and to insert, also perpendicular to the beam, a wedge of air or glass. Localized fringes then appear in the wedge. Two light beams emerging from the etalons with some small path

* This assumes the simple case of an air-filled etalon surrounded by air.

difference may have this path difference compensated for by means of the wedge, since part of the longer beam passes straight through the wedge, while part of the shorter one suffers a double reflection and thus has its path increased a little. The zero-order fringe appears where the total paths are exactly equal.

Haidinger's fringes are fringes of constant inclination produced by a thick, parallel-sided glass plate (or a Fabry-Pérot etalon) which are viewable directly by means of the eye. It is possible to see such fringes only when viewing in the normal direction,* so that a small range of light directions near the normal is accepted by the eye. At larger angles of inclination the relative sideways displacement of the interfering beams (e.g., AB in Fig. 5F) is of such magnitude that the eye aperture is unable to accept these beams together, and thus the interference effects are not seen. A wider-aperture telescopic system should in principle allow the equal inclination fringes to be seen at larger inclinations; with thick plates and etalons, however, the higher inclination fringes are so closely spaced as to be invisible. Thinner plates and films allow equal inclination fringes to be seen at larger inclinations to the normal, both by the eye and by telescopic systems.

Applications of thin-film interference effects

Examination of surfaces. An experiment which is easily performed in the laboratory will be described as an introduction to an account of some methods of examination of surfaces based on thin-film interference effects. The apparatus for this experiment is arranged as shown in Fig. 5K. Two sheets of plate glass B and C are arranged horizontally, one resting on the other. A thin air-film exists between the plates, since neither of the adjacent faces is perfectly flat. A diffusing screen placed in front of a sodium lamp forms an extended source of sodium light. By means of the glass plate A, held at 45° to the vertical, some of this light is reflected into directions near the normal to the air-film between the plates B and C. The beams reflected at the air-film surfaces return vertically and, in part, pass through the plate A and enter the eye. The arrangement of the glass plate A and the diffuse source to the side is a simple means of providing

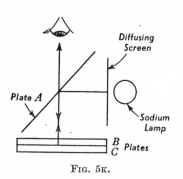

Diffusing Screen

Plate A

Sodium Lamp

B Plates C

FIG. 5K.

* The arrangement of Fig. 5K, with the thick glass plate replacing the air film, would be needed to observe Haidinger fringes in reflected light. They may be viewed in transmitted light directly through a Fabry–Pérot etalon.

light in near-normal directions without interrupting the viewing of the reflected effects. Localized fringes are seen in the vicinity of the air-film, and the conditions for cancellation and reinforcement of the interfering wave systems are

$$2e = m\lambda \qquad \text{cancellation}$$

and $\qquad 2e = (m + \tfrac{1}{2})\lambda \qquad$ reinforcement.

These are the simple forms of the equations 5.2a and 5.2b when $n = 1$ and cos ϕ may be taken as 1. The appearance of the fringe system depends on the form of the air-film between the surfaces, and it is possible to deduce the latter in view of the following considerations. In the first place any one fringe, dark or bright, corresponds to a constant integral value of m in the relevant equation of the two quoted above, and thus to a constant value of e. Each fringe is thus a locus of constant air-film thickness. Fringes of this nature are frequently referred to as *fringes of equal optical thickness*. Secondly, consecutive fringes of the same sort correspond to a change in m by unity in the relevant equation above. This evidently corresponds to a change in e of $\lambda/2$. For points through which consecutive fringes of the same sort pass, the air-film therefore differs in thickness by half the wavelength of the light employed. Thus the fringe system forms a kind of contour map of the air-film thickness between the plates. If one of the plates were absolutely flat, then the shape of the other plate would be indicated by interpretation of the fringe pattern seen.

The fringe system viewed with the arrangement shown in Fig. 5K may vary considerably in appearance, depending on the forms of the adjacent faces of the glass plates B and C. Fig. 5L shows a possible set of fringes and its interpretation along the line PQ. Pressure on the two plates at the point R, so as to reduce the air-film thickness there, enables a conclusion to be formed as to one point which is not revealed by the form of the fringes alone, namely, whether the air-film thickness has its highest or lowest value at R. If the outer fringes approach R when this is done, it is evident that they must correspond to smaller thicknesses than that existent at R in the first place, i.e., the film must be thickest at R. Conversely, fringes which recede from R must correspond to higher thicknesses than that at R.

A further point is evident from Fig. 5L. The spacing of the interference fringes is related to the steepness of the air-film thickness variation, the fringes being spaced well apart when the film thickness changes very gradually, and vice versa. If the closeness of fit of the two surfaces of B and C is such that the air-film does not vary in thickness by more than a few multiples of $\lambda/2$ over the whole area of the plates, then only a few fringes are seen. If the two surfaces were a perfect fit, the dark minimum corresponding to $m = 0$ would be so broad as to occupy the whole area viewed. Plane surfaces are said to be *optically flat* if this occurs, as far as can be judged, when two such surfaces are in contact. Their shapes are sufficiently close to perfect planes that the difference is not detectable by these optical-interference methods, and the actual departures from perfect flatness are not more than one-tenth of light wavelengths in magnitude. High-quality optical flats may be much more perfect than this.

In the process of grinding of lens or prism faces the shape of the surface concerned may be examined at any stage in a manner essentially similar to that described above. A further surface is used, having a form such that the surface being ground will fit it very closely when it is of the required shape, and the grinding process is continued until

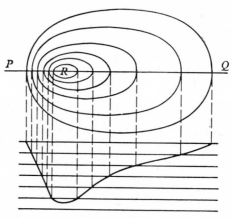

Fig. 5L.

the interference pattern seen indicates that the surface is sufficiently close to the desired form.

When the two adjacent glass surfaces of Fig. 5K are respectively plane and spherical in shape, a system of interference fringes known as *Newton's rings* is obtained. A lens (often with a convex long-radius lower surface) resting on an optically flat surface is usually employed in order to produce these rings. The fringes are circular, and the difference between the squares of the radii of consecutive fringes is constant. If necessary, the radius of the curved face may be found from measurements on the rings.

A further special example is the case of the fringes produced by the air-wedge between two optically flat surfaces which are spaced apart at one side by insertion of some very thin object. The fringes are then equally spaced straight lines parallel to the apex of the wedge. Measurements on their spacing lead to a value for the angle of the wedge, from which the thickness of the inserted object may be determined. Such methods are very suitable for measurements of small distances not easily determinable otherwise, e.g., diameters of quartz fibres, and thicknesses of mechanical gauges.

Fizeau developed a method for measurement of expansion coefficients in which the small increment in length of a solid was measured by interference methods such as those just described. In Fig. 5M, *B* and *C* represent the
bounding surfaces of an air-wedge. If the plate
having *C* as one of its faces is attached perpendicularly to the expanding rod so that it

Fig. 5M.

moves to *C'* as the expansion takes place, it is clear that this movement is accompanied by movement of the whole fringe pattern in a direction perpendicular to the line fringes. The pattern is displaced by a distance equal to the separation of the fringes for a movement of *C* equal to $\lambda/2$. Thus the number of fringes passing some fixed point in the field of view (usually located by the cross-wires of a microscope focused on the fringes) indicates the distance moved by *C*.

Fig. 5N indicates in its essentials the instrument known as the *Fizeau interferometer*, which is employed to produce fringes of constant optical thickness for testing of surfaces. A small source *S* in the focal plane of a lens pro-
duces a parallel beam of light incident almost normally upon the thin air film. The eye is placed at the point at which the returning beams focus after passage through the lens, these beams being diverted through a right angle before they focus, by means of a prism arranged as shown. The whole area of the reflect-
ing film is seen through the lens, and is uniform in illumination only if the optical thickness of the film is constant. An interference pattern appears if this is not so. With an arrangement such as this, light within a very narrow range of angles of incidence falls on the film and is received by the eye. This makes possible the viewing of fringes even when the thickness *e* of the reflecting film is considerable. It is evident that since the path difference for the thin film of refractive index *n* is $ne \cos \phi$ (ϕ being the refraction angle within the film), small variations in ϕ are of more serious effect with thicker films. Such an arrangement could evidently be employed to test the constancy of *ne* for a sheet of glass, i.e., to test its parallelism and homogeneity.

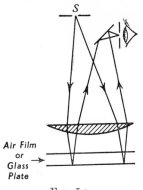

Air Film or Glass Plate →

Fig. 5N.

Fringes of equal optical thickness are often spoken of as *Fizeau fringes*, since arrangements in which the incident light is collimated, so that the intensity changes are entirely due to optical thickness variations, were first employed by Fizeau.

In recent years *Tolansky* has developed methods of examination of surfaces which are essentially similar to those already described, but using highly reflecting surfaces obtained by deposition of silver or other metallic films upon the surfaces under examination. The transmission maxima are extremely sharp in such cases, since multiple-reflection interference effects are involved, and as a result very small variations in optical thickness can much more readily be detected. Consider, as a simple example, the interference pattern shown in Fig. 50. Let the full lines represent the positions of the intensity maxima in the interference pattern. A small discontinuity in one of the faces,

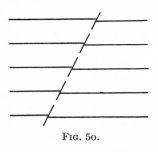

running in the direction of the dotted line, would appear as an abrupt break in the continuity of the fringes. The ease with which this may be detected depends on the sharpness of the bright fringes. It is evident from the figure that discontinuities of very small fractions of a wavelength can be detected and their magnitudes estimated provided the interference maxima are very sharp. Tolansky has used such methods for examining the topography of crystal and other surfaces, and details having magnitudes of the order of 10 Å are discernible under good conditions (reference 14).

FIG. 50.

Anti-reflection films.—The process known as " coating " or " blooming " of surfaces of lenses and other optical components is an example of the utilization of interference effects of thin films. It is desirable that light reflected at surfaces of lenses, etc., should be reduced to a minimum so that the illumination of the images formed by transmitted light should be as high as possible. For normal incidence about 4 per cent. of the light incident on a single air/glass surface is reflected, and it is readily seen that, as a consequence, images produced by optical systems containing several such surfaces are considerably diminished in intensity. The coating process overcomes this disadvantage in the following way. A thin film of transparent material having optical thickness (i.e., ne) equal to $\lambda/4$, and of refractive index less than that of glass, is deposited on each glass surface. This case is different from those previously considered, since the refractive index increases in the incident-light direction across both boundaries of the film, assuming the light to be incident in the air as shown in Fig. 5P. If, on the other hand, a rear surface of a lens is under consideration, the refractive index decreases across both surfaces in the direction of incidence of the light. In the former case change of phase on reflection occurs at both interfaces, in the latter case at neither. Thus change of phase on reflection does not affect the phase *difference* between the returning beams in either case. Since the optical thickness of the deposited film is $\lambda/4$, the path difference between the normally reflected beams is $\lambda/2$ and the beams are out of phase. Perfect cancellation occurs if the amplitudes of the returning beams are exactly equal. It may be shown that, for an interface between two media a and b, the reflected beam has a fraction r of the amplitude of the incident beam such that for normal incidence

$$r = \frac{n_a - n_b}{n_a + n_b}$$

Employing this expression and letting n_a, n_f, n_g be the refractive indices of the air, film, and glass, it is easily shown that the condition that the two reflected amplitudes should be equal is

$$n_f{}^2 = n_a n_g$$

This is approximately true for film materials such as cryolite (sodium aluminium fluoride) or magnesium fluoride, which, because of their suitability in this and other respects, are the materials generally used.

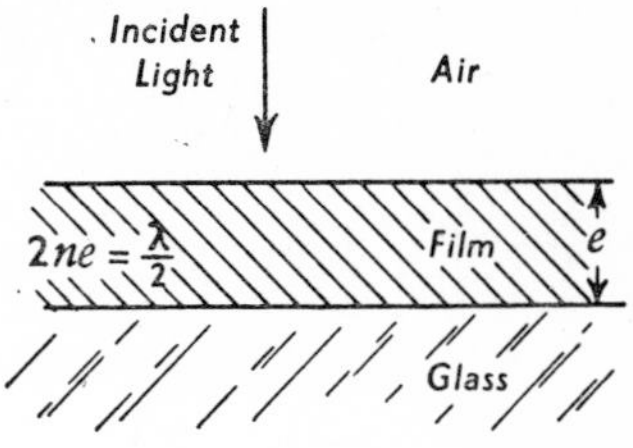

FIG. 5P.

The optical thickness can only be $\lambda/4$ for one wavelength, so that less complete reduction in intensity of reflected light of other wavelengths occurs. The thickness is chosen for optimum transmission of light near the wavelength of maximum visual sensitivity. The purple " bloomed " appearance of surfaces coated in this way is due to the residual reflected light in the red and blue spectral regions.

High-reflection films.—The reverse of the above-mentioned effect, i.e., increase rather than decrease of the reflected light, may be achieved by coating a glass surface with a film of high-refractive-index material of $\lambda/4$ optical thickness. If n_f is higher than both n_a and n_g, phase reversal on reflection occurs at one only of the faces of the film, and this, together with the phase difference between the normally-incident reflected beams due to the film thickness, results in the reinforcement of these beams. The reflected fraction of the incident light is higher the more n_f exceeds n_a and n_g. The choice of suitable film materials for use in this way is limited. Zinc sulphide ($n = 2\cdot3$) has been frequently used.

Still higher values for the reflected fraction of the incident light may be obtained by depositing a number of successive films upon a glass surface. Fig. 5Q shows an example of such a multi-layer reflecting film. Alternate layers of high- and low-refractive-index materials are used in the way shown, the optical thicknesses of each being made equal to $\lambda/4$. It is evident on consideration, bearing in mind that change of phase on reflection occurs only at the interfaces across which the refractive index increases, that the reflected waves from all the faces are in phase. With three layers, arranged as shown, about two-thirds of the incident light may be expected to be reflected, and this expectation is borne out in practice. Still more layers may be used, with consequent improvement in the reflecting power. Such reflecting surfaces are more satisfactory than silvered or other metal-coated surfaces, since better reflecting power is obtainable, and the complications arising with metal-coated surfaces due to absorption are less pronounced. Improvements have been made in the performance of interference filters and Fabry–Pérot interferometers (see pp. 90 and 122) when the usual metal coatings have been replaced by multiple dielectric films.

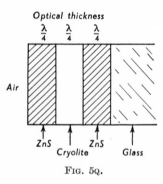

Optical thickness
$\frac{\lambda}{4}$ $\frac{\lambda}{4}$ $\frac{\lambda}{4}$

Air

ZnS   ZnS
  Cryolite   Glass

FIG. 5Q.

White light and heterochromatic fringes.—Little has been said regarding the effects observed when interferometric devices are illuminated with white light. The effects so far discussed for a single wavelength then occur for the whole range of incident wavelengths. With a double-slit arrangement, for example, the $\cos^2 \gamma$ intensity variation (where $\gamma = \frac{\pi}{\lambda}(a+b)\sin\theta$, see pp. 11 and 42) in both red and blue light is represented on the same scale of θ in Fig. 5R. The pattern is symmetrical about the $\theta = 0$ axis. The resultant intensity effect is evidently that obtained by superposing similar intensity curves for all the wavelengths present. Where the phase difference is zero the zero order maxima of all the patterns superpose, giving a white central maximum. Elsewhere the maxima in the patterns are separated; and, in all regions appreciably removed from the zero order, the overlapping of the fringes is so great that it is impossible to distinguish them. A few low-order coloured fringes are distinguishable, the blue coloration in any order being towards the central white fringe and the red away from it, and the other colours intermediate.

With near-monochromatic light many interference fringes are produced by a simple interferometer, and it is often difficult to detect any difference between the maxima of the different orders. On substituting a white source, only low-order fringes are discernible, and when the single white fringe is in view the optical paths of the interfering beams to the point where this fringe appears are known to be equal. The possibility of making adjustments so that this is the case is a necessary part of certain applications of interferometry (see Chapter 8).

In the regions of higher-order interference, where the overlapping of the interference patterns makes the fringes indistinguishable, the spectral nature of the light at any position in the field may be complicated. As a simple example, imagine the slit of a spectroscope placed

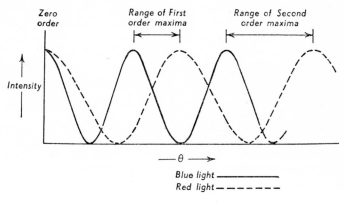

FIG. 5R.

in the field of a Young's double-slit interferometer so that it coincides with the position of the 10th order maximum when sodium light of wavelength 5890 Å is used. Consider the effect of substituting a white-light source in place of the sodium illumination. Two beams arrive at the slit, the path difference between them being 10×5890 Å. The beams of any other wavelength λ, such that this path difference is an integral multiple m of λ, also fully reinforce at the slit. On the other hand, the beams of wavelengths such that $(m + \frac{1}{2})\lambda$ is just equal to the path difference cancel at the slit. The spectrum seen through the spectroscope therefore shows alternate maxima and minima in intensity with wavelength. The maximum values occur at $\dfrac{58900 \text{ Å}}{m}$ and the minima at $\dfrac{58900 \text{ Å}}{(m + \frac{1}{2})}$, where m has various suitable integral values such that the wavelengths concerned fall within the visible region.

D

This is a simple example of the type of interference fringes known as *heterochromatic fringes*.

A parallel-sided air-film with silvered surfaces, placed over the slit of a spectroscope, illuminated by white light passing normally through the film, produces a similar appearance in the spectrum because of the path difference $2e$ between the beams transmitted by such an arrangement. Wavelengths such that $2e = m\lambda$ are most intense, whereas those for which $2e = (m + \frac{1}{2})\lambda$ show intensity minima. Consecutive fringes of the same sort correspond to unit change of order m, and it is easily shown that Δk, the change in wave-number k $\left(= \dfrac{1}{\lambda} \right)$ between consecutive fringes, is $1/2e$. A method of calibration of a spectroscope by focusing on the consecutive fringes, making use of this fact, was first used by Edser and Butler. If the air-film with silvered surfaces is not parallel-sided, the quantity e varies along the length of the slit, so that the maximum and minimum intensity features in the spectrum are no longer parallel to the slit, i.e., no longer vertical. If a wedge-shaped air-film is used, so that e varies uniformly along the slit, these fringes are inclined at an angle to the vertical. Generally the fringes are such that $\dfrac{e}{\lambda}$ is constant, and equal to $m/2$, for bright fringes, m taking consecutive integral values. Every fringe therefore represents the section of the air-film along the slit length. Use of highly silvered surfaces sharpens the bright fringes. Tolansky has termed these *fringes of equal chromatic order* and has used them, in addition to fringes of the Fizeau type, for the investigation of forms of surfaces of crystals and other structures. The method is rather more powerful for the detection of very small surface discontinuities.

Interference filters.—The principles of the production of heterochromatic fringes, discussed in the foregoing paragraph, form the basis of the construction of devices known as interference filters, i.e., devices for passing a narrow band of wavelengths making use of interference rather than absorption for removing the undesired wavelengths.

Maxima in the normally-transmitted light for a thin film of thickness e and refractive index n occur for wavelengths such that

$$2ne = m\lambda$$

If e is many times greater than λ several integral values of m may correspond to visible wavelengths in this expression, and a corresponding number of intensity maxima appear in the spectrum of the transmitted light. The smaller e, the greater the spacing of these maxima and the fewer occur in the visible region. With a very thin film only one maximum of intensity may occur in the visible region, and the film then acts as a filter transmitting light only in the immediate vicinity of this wavelength. The simplest case is that in which $m = 1$ in the above expression and ne, the optical thickness of the film, is made equal to $\lambda/2$, where λ is the wavelength at which maximum transmission is desired. The sharpness of the band of wavelengths transmitted depends on the quality of the reflecting surfaces bounding the film forming the filter. The half-width of the band passed by good-quality interference filters with metal-deposited surfaces is of the order 100 Å. This is a narrower wavelength range than can be selected by most ordinary coloured filters acting by absorption. Other advantages are that transmission in any desired region of the spectrum may be obtained by appropriate choice of film thickness; and the percentage transmission at the peak wavelength of the pass-band is generally better than can be obtained by other means.

Using multi-layer dielectric reflecting films, still better peak transmission and sharpness of the transmission curve are obtainable. Half-widths of about 20 Å at 6000 Å have been obtained.

CHAPTER 6

DIFFRACTION AND THE PROPERTIES OF OPTICAL INSTRUMENTS

SINCE there are necessary limits to the sizes of apertures of visual optical instruments, it follows that, due to diffraction, the images formed by them can never be perfect even if the imperfections due to residual aberrations of the lenses, etc., could be entirely removed. Also, because of the existence of these diffraction effects, images formed by systems with definite residual aberrations may, within certain limits, be no more imperfect than those which would be formed by a system perfectly corrected for aberrations. These facts have a bearing on the resolution limits of optical instruments such as telescopes and microscopes, and also on the optical-aberration tolerances permissible in design of good optical components. A basic discussion of these matters is given in this chapter. The idea of the resolution limit obtainable with optical instruments of a dispersive nature is also introduced here, by reference to simple cases, since the basis of the understanding of this matter has much in common with that underlying resolution of image-forming instruments.

Resolving power of microscopes and telescopes

The image of a point object produced by an aberration-free system.—Fig. 6A shows spherical waves originating at an object point U and

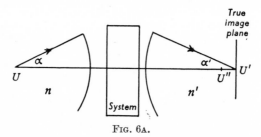

FIG. 6A.

entering an optical system. The system is considered to be free from aberration, so that the emergent waves are spherical about U', which is the image point conjugate with U according to simple considerations of geometrical optics. The aperture limits the extent of the wavefronts passed and, for reasons explained in Chapter 4, a diffraction pattern is produced in the vicinity of U'. The amplitude at any point near U' in the transverse plane through U' is the resultant of the contributions there from all parts of the transmitted wave-front. If the aperture is circular the pattern is radially symmetrical about U'. The resultant amplitude (and hence the intensity) at any particular transverse distance from U' is obtained by a process of vectorial addition essentially similar to tnat described on p. 52. The pattern corresponding to the point object consists of a circular patch which falls off in intensity away from the ideal image point U' at its centre, surrounded by outer rings, alternately dark and bright, the bright rings becoming rapidly fainter the larger their radii. Along any radius in the pattern the intensity falls to zero at the first dark ring, and the part of the pattern within this ring is known as the *Airy disc*.

It may be shown generally that y', the radius of the first dark ring for light of wavelength λ, is given by

$$y' = \frac{0 \cdot 61\lambda}{n' \sin \alpha'} \qquad \cdots \cdots \quad \textbf{6.1}$$

the meaning of the symbols being indicated in Fig. 6A. Equation 3.5 is the special form taken by this relation when plane waves are emergent from the system, θ being the angular radius of the first minimum in the pattern. It must be emphasized that equation 6.1 applies only to the pattern in the transverse plane through the ideal image point, the system concerned being aberrationless.

The distance y' in the image plane corresponds to a distance y in the object plane through U, given by

$$y = \frac{0 \cdot 61\lambda}{n \sin \alpha} \cdot \qquad \cdots \cdots \quad \textbf{6.2}$$

This must be the case, since the transverse linear magnification y'/y corresponding to the pair of conjugate planes considered must be the same for light through all parts of the aperture of such an aberration-free system, its magnitude being given by the optical sine relation, $ny \sin \alpha = n'y' \sin \alpha'$.

The Rayleigh criterion of resolution.—It is evident that an image made up of small diffraction patterns, each corresponding to a point in the object plane, is not a perfect reproduction of the object. Object points near enough together must produce diffraction patterns which overlap, and if the overlapping is considerable they may not be separately distinguishable. There is thus a limit to the closeness of points in the object which will be reproduced in such a way as to be seen separately in the image. Rayleigh proposed a criterion for the limit of resolution of details in optical images, as follows. He considered that two identical diffraction patterns of the kind just discussed are just distinguishable when the separation of their centres is equal to the radius of the first dark ring of either of them.   Fig. 6B shows two intensity patterns which are just resolved according to this criterion. The broken line indicates the intensity variation along the line joining the centres of the patterns.   An alternative way of expressing the Rayleigh criterion is that the intensity mid-way between the two pattern centres must not be more than 0·81 of the central intensity in either pattern, if the impression of a double image is to be gained.

If the Rayleigh criterion is adopted, the radius y' given by equation 6.1 is also the minimum separation of the ideal image points corresponding to two object points which are just distinguished in the image.   Thus y, in equation 6.2, is the nearest distance of object points which may be resolved.   Since equations 6.1 and 6.2 apply to aberration-free systems, poorer resolution performance than is indicated by

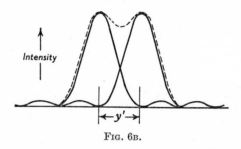

FIG. 6B.

these equations will result if the system actually used is inadequately corrected for aberrations.   The images of point objects are then of larger size than the ideal diffraction patterns, and need to be correspondingly farther apart in order to be distinguished.

Equation 6.2, and others derived from it later, merely indicate the resolution limit obtainable by improvement of the quality of an optical system.   The Rayleigh criterion only roughly defines the limit of closeness of two diffraction patterns distinguishable by the eye.   To the normal eye slightly better resolution than that indicated by this criterion is possible when the images being observed are similar in intensity.*   The effect of inequality in the intensities of the two images is to increase the separation necessary for resolution.   It is evident also that resolution depends on the wavelength, being better for the shorter wavelengths.   Use of the wavelength of maximum visual

---

* Non-visual photoelectric techniques may be made to emphasize a much shallower intensity depression between the two diffraction-pattern centres, and thus to go considerably beyond the optimum capability of the eye in detecting the dual nature of the combined intensity pattern which is the image of a pair of close objects.

sensitivity in equation 6.2 gives a rough single figure for the resolution limit of a visual instrument transmitting white light.

In the deduction of equation 6.2 the assumption is made that the *intensities* in the two overlapping diffraction patterns simply add together, and thus cause the difficulty in recognizing visually the double nature of the total effect when the patterns are too close. This is true only if no constant phase relation exists between the two object sources to which the patterns correspond, i.e., if the object points concerned are completely incoherent. When coherence conditions exist between the object points considered, the *amplitudes* add vectorially at any place in the image plane where the corresponding patterns overlap, i.e., interference takes place there. It is evident that the resulting intensity pattern may differ from that obtained with incoherent objects. With some types of instrument, e.g., microscopes, the object points are not self-luminous and therefore not incoherent, and this is an additional reason why the above equations do not give the precise resolution limit.

A simple discussion of resolving power of telescopes and microscopes, assuming self-luminous objects, now follows. The Abbe theory of microscopic vision, which takes into account the object coherence conditions, is discussed in the following chapter.

Resolving power of microscopes.—The resolving power of a microscope is defined as the smallest transverse linear separation of object points which are seen distinctly in the image. For an instrument with a well-corrected objective this is given directly by equation 6.2. The quantity $n \sin \alpha$ is often referred to as the *numerical aperture* of the microscope (denoted by N.A.), where n is the refractive index in the object space and α the extreme inclination to the axis of transmitted rays from the axial object point.

Thus
$$\text{Resolving power} = \frac{0.61\lambda}{(\text{N.A.})} \quad . \quad . \quad . \quad . \quad \textbf{6.3}$$

In Chapter 7 it will be shown that because of the conditions of illumination of the object the factor 0·61 is incorrect and, with suitable condensing arrangements, the highest possible resolution is given by the expression

$$\text{Resolving power} = \frac{\lambda}{2(\text{N.A.})} \quad . \quad . \quad . \quad . \quad \textbf{6.4}$$

With the highest numerical apertures (1–1·5) details of dimensions of about half the wavelength of light used are therefore detectable.

A further point must also be considered. Under constant-illumination conditions the eye lens has a definite aperture, and diffraction occurs at this aperture. It also has certain residual optical aberrations at any particular aperture. Furthermore, the individual receptors lying side by side in the retinal surface upon which images are cast each have a definite small, though not infinitesimal, area. These facts combine to set a limit to the resolution of an image seen by the eye. The *resolving power of the eye* is usually defined as the least angular separation of a pair of points which may be seen separate by the eye. The figure of *one minute of arc* is usually quoted for its approximate magnitude for the normal eye under average illumination conditions. Thus, in the image formed by the objective of a microscope, diffraction patterns at the minimum separation for resolution are seen separately only if the image is viewed so that they subtend an angle at the eye of more than one minute of arc. In practice, this means using an eye-piece of sufficient power, so that the images of object points separated by the closest resolvable distance subtend a large enough angle at the eye. If a lower-power eyepiece is used, the eye rather than the aperture of the objective limits the detail viewable, and poorer resolution than that indicated by equation 6.3 is obtained. Similar considerations arise with telescopes.

Resolving power of telescopes.—While the minimum distance in the object plane which can be resolved is the most suitable measure of the resolving power of a microscope, an angular measure is best suited for the statement of the resolving power of the eye and of telescopes. Let l be the object distance from the objective, and θ the angle subtended at the objective by the minimum resolvable transverse distance y. Distant objects are almost always viewed by telescopes, so that the approximation $\theta = y/l$ is very close.

Thus, from equation 6.2, $\theta = \dfrac{0 \cdot 61\lambda}{nl \sin \alpha}$

Let d be the diameter of the objective. Then, since l is large, $\sin \alpha = \dfrac{d}{2l}$, and the resolving power

$$\theta = \frac{1 \cdot 22\lambda}{nd} \quad . \quad . \quad . \quad . \quad . \quad \textbf{6.5}$$

The refractive index n in the object space is almost invariably unity for a telescope.

Objects viewed by a telescope, though separated by a small angle, are normally at considerable actual distances apart, and thus act as quite independent sources. The resolving power obtained assuming incoherent sources is therefore satisfactory for telescopes.

The Rayleigh limit and optical tolerances

The image of a point object formed by an aberration-free system of circular aperture, described in the previous section, is of such a kind that the precise determination of the true image plane (conjugate with the transverse plane through the object) would be very difficult. The appearance of the image on planes longitudinally displaced from the true image plane, while not quite the same as that in the true plane, may constitute a no less sufficiently satisfactory image of the point object over a certain small range of positions of the image plane. Movement of the plane on which the image is formed away from the ideal image plane (e.g., from U' to U'' in Fig. 6A) means that the optical paths to the centre of the pattern are no longer all equal. U', for instance, is the centre of the emergent spherical waves in Fig. 6A, and the paths through the system from U to U' are all equal. Various paths through the system from U to U'' cannot also be all equal. It is evident therefore that there must be a maximum range of path lengths from U to U'' if the pattern around U'' is to be not appreciably poorer in sharpness and quality than the ideal pattern around U'. It is also clear that a real optical system with imperfect aberration-correction may produce an image of a point object which is as satisfactory as any obtainable with an ideal system, provided the residual aberrations are within certain small limits. Imperfect aberration-correction means that the emergent waves corresponding to a point object are not quite spherical in shape, so that the paths through the system to the ideal image point, or to any point near it, are unequal to some extent. Provided the range of optical paths is small enough, the image may be as satisfactory as it is possible to obtain. Rayleigh suggested that for the image quality to remain not seriously impaired because of the existence of unequal paths through the system, the range of optical paths should not exceed one-quarter of the wavelength of the light being refracted. The so-called *Rayleigh $\lambda/4$ limit* is a useful guide for the estimation of tolerable residual aberrations in optical systems; reduction of the aberrations below these limits is not necessary, since there is no corresponding improvement in the image.

The permissible aberrations, based on the Rayleigh $\lambda/4$ limit, are frequently considerably different from those estimated by the methods of pure geometrical optics, i.e., by considering the sections of beams of light rays near the position where the image is focused. It is therefore important that wave-optical aspects of image formation should be borne in mind in assessing the expected performance of any proposed design of optical component.

The validity of Rayleigh's assumption, that an optical path range of not more than $\lambda/4$ causes no serious deterioration in the appearance of the image, depends on circumstances. The choice of $\lambda/4$ as the limiting tolerable path difference is as good a single specification of this quantity as possible, this magnitude being about correct in very many cases of image formation by practical optical systems. There are, however,

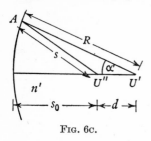

FIG. 6c.

exceptional cases in which a somewhat larger magnitude is tolerable, and others for which even the quarter-wave limit is excessive.

The longitudinal range of focus (for an aberration-free system) is obtainable from the limiting tolerable optical path range by reference to Fig. 6c. In this figure U' is the centre of curvature of an emergent spherical wave-front of radius R; U'' is the inward limit of the tolerable range of focus; α' is the semi-angular aperture of the system in the image space; s is the distance to U'' from the point A on the margin of the wave-front, and s_0 the distance to U'' from the pole of the wave-front. The distance $U'U''$ is denoted by d.

Then
$$s^2 = R^2 + d^2 - 2Rd \cos \alpha'$$

Also, since
$$R = s_0 + d$$
$$s_0{}^2 = R^2 + d^2 - 2Rd$$

Thus
$$s^2 - s_0{}^2 = 2Rd(1 - \cos \alpha')$$

And, taking
$$s + s_0 = 2R,$$
$$s - s_0 = d(1 - \cos \alpha')$$

The range of optical paths is $n'(s - s_0)$, n' being the refractive index in the image space.

When this is equal to $\lambda/4$,

$$d = \frac{\lambda}{4n'(1 - \cos \alpha')} \quad \cdot \quad \cdot \quad \cdot \quad \cdot \quad \textbf{6.6}$$

The approximation $\sin^2 \alpha' = 2(1 - \cos \alpha')$ is sufficiently close up to values of α' of $30°$ to $40°$, and equation 6.6 is therefore frequently written

$$d = \frac{\lambda}{2n' \sin^2 \alpha'} \quad \cdot \quad \cdot \quad \cdot \quad \cdot \quad \cdot \quad \cdot \quad \textbf{6.7}$$

This gives the tolerable longitudinal departure in either direction from the true image position. Reference 3 may be consulted for detailed application of the $\lambda/4$ limit to the estimation of aberration tolerances. Examples of misleading predictions of ray-optics methods in such matters as depth of focus of optical instruments are also given there.

Resolving power of dispersive instruments

Instruments which disperse light do so by producing deviation of the light, which is dependent in amount upon the wavelength. If no limits to the apertures of such instruments existed, the direction of the emergent beam of any precise wavelength would be well defined. Because of the inevitable aperture limits occurring in practice, however, diffraction takes place; and the light of any one wavelength emerges over a range of directions, usually falling off in intensity sharply away from the principal emergent direction for this wavelength. Because of this, a limit is set to the closeness of a pair of wavelengths which can be effectively separated by any instrument of this sort.

If $\Delta\lambda$ is the closest wavelength spacing which may be resolved, the wavelength in the spectral region concerned being λ, the quantity $\lambda/\Delta\lambda$ is a quantitative measure of the wavelength-resolution capabilities of the instrument and is known as its *resolving power*.

The ideas underlying resolution properties of dispersive devices are now illustrated by derivations of resolving power of plane gratings and prisms. Similar considerations are necessary with other dispersive instruments; these are introduced where appropriate in later chapters.

Plane gratings.—The principal maxima in the interference pattern formed by a regularly-arranged series of slits, when light is incident perpendicular to the plane containing the slits, occur in such directions that

$$(a + b) \sin \theta = m\lambda \quad \text{(see pp. 42 and 48)}$$

The equation 3.4 gives the angular half-width $\Delta\theta$ of each of the principal maxima when the total number of slit apertures is N.

$$\Delta\theta = \frac{\lambda}{N(a + b) \cos \theta} \quad \cdot \quad \cdot \quad \cdot \quad \cdot \quad \cdot \quad 3.4$$

Since the aperture of the grating is limited, N has a finite magnitude, so that $\Delta\theta$ is not infinitesimally small. The form of the intensity distribution within the principal maxima is indicated in Fig. 3K (iii), and PQ in that figure corresponds to the half-width $\Delta\theta$ of equation 3.4.

Consider now two close wavelengths λ and $\lambda + \Delta\lambda$ incident upon the grating. The intensity distribution corresponding to the second wavelength will be similar in form to the curve of Fig. 3K (iii) but rather different in horizontal scale. The principal maxima (in all but the zero order) will therefore be separated; and, adopting the Rayleigh criterion for resolution, must be at least PQ (Fig. 3K (iii)) apart in order to be distinguishable. The angular half-width $\Delta\theta$ must therefore not exceed the angle of dispersion between the wavelengths λ and $\lambda + \Delta\lambda$, if resolution is to be obtained.

Differentiation of $(a + b) \sin \theta = m\lambda$

yields
$$\frac{d\theta}{d\lambda} = \frac{m}{(a + b) \cos \theta} \cdot \qquad \cdots \qquad \textbf{6.8}$$

The wavelengths λ and $\lambda + \Delta\lambda$ are therefore separated by an angle $\dfrac{m}{(a + b) \cos \theta} \cdot \Delta\lambda$ after dispersion by the grating. The condition for resolution is thus

$$\frac{m}{(a + b) \cos \theta} \cdot \Delta\lambda \geqslant \frac{\lambda}{N(a + b) \cos \theta}$$

or
$$\frac{\lambda}{\Delta\lambda} \leqslant mN \qquad \cdots \qquad \textbf{6.9}$$

Comments on the expressions 6.8 and 6.9 appear shortly along with those on the corresponding expressions for a prism.

Prisms.—As with a grating, determination of the resolving power of a prism follows from two considerations. Understanding of the principles by which the prism produces dispersion permits an expression for $\dfrac{d\theta}{d\lambda}$ to be found; so that the angular separation of a pair of close wavelengths is known. Secondly, the spread of direction of the emergent light of any one wavelength, due to diffraction, must be considered in connection with this.

Consider the part of a parallel beam of light falling over the portion AB of the first face of a prism, as shown in Fig. 6D. BB' is an incident

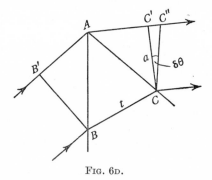

Fig. 6D.

wave-front. Let CC' be the corresponding emergent wave-front for light of wavelength λ, for which the refractive index of the prism is μ. By the principle of equal optical paths

$$B'A + AC' = \mu BC = \mu t$$

The positions of C and C' and the magnitude of μ vary with wavelength. Thus, differentiating,

$$\Delta(AC') = t \cdot \Delta\mu + \mu \cdot \Delta t$$

The form of the dispersion relation for a prism is such that if C is assumed to be unaltered in distance from B (i.e., $\Delta t = 0$) and the new position C'' of C' considered as remaining on the line AC', the differences between the true paths and those assumed in this way are of the second order only, and may be neglected. The above expression may therefore be written

$$C'C'' = t \cdot \Delta\mu$$

The wavelengths λ and $\lambda + \Delta\lambda$ advance after dispersion in directions perpendicular to CC' and CC''; so that $\Delta\theta$, the angular separation of these wavelengths, is $C'CC''$. If a is the breadth CC' of the emergent wave-fronts, a quantity dependent on the size of the prism and the way in which it is placed in the original beam, then $C'C'' = a \cdot \Delta\theta$.

Thus
$$\frac{d\theta}{d\mu} = \frac{t}{a}$$

or
$$\frac{d\theta}{d\lambda} = \frac{t}{a} \cdot \frac{d\mu}{d\lambda} \quad \cdot \quad \cdot \quad \cdot \quad \cdot \quad \cdot \quad \textbf{6.10}$$

The angular separation of the wavelengths λ and $\lambda + \Delta\lambda$ is therefore

$$\Delta\theta = \frac{t}{a} \cdot \frac{d\mu}{d\lambda} \cdot \Delta\lambda$$

Consider now the single wavelength λ only. Maximum intensity occurs for this wavelength in the direction perpendicular to CC', but spreading about this direction occurs because of the finite breadth a of the emergent wave-front. The angular half-width of the emergent beam of this wavelength will be just $\Delta\theta$ if $C'C'' = \lambda$, since the waves of length λ in the direction perpendicular to CC'' will produce zero intensity in the manner described on p. 51, when this is so. If $C'C'' > \lambda$ the angle $\Delta\theta$ will be greater than the angular half-width of the beam of wavelength λ. Adopting the Rayleigh criterion, the condition for resolution is therefore $C'C'' \geqslant \lambda$, or $a\Delta\theta \geqslant \lambda$.

Using the value $\Delta\theta$ above, this may be written

$$\frac{\lambda}{\Delta\lambda} \leqslant t \cdot \frac{d\mu}{d\lambda} \quad \cdot \quad \cdot \quad \cdot \quad \cdot \quad \cdot \quad \textbf{6.11}$$

The resolving power of a prism is directly dependent on $\dfrac{d\mu}{d\lambda}$, as might be expected. In addition to this, it depends only on t. For optimum resolution a prism must be so placed relative to the incident light that

t is as large as possible, i.e., so that full use is made of the faces of the prism.   Prisms of the same glass of any triangular shape have the same resolving power if the length of their bases is constant and is fully utilized in each case.

Both $\dfrac{d\theta}{d\lambda}$ and the resolving power vary with wavelength for prisms, since $\dfrac{d\mu}{d\lambda}$ is wavelength-dependent.   Inconstant dispersion and resolution throughout the spectrum, both of which are much higher towards short wavelengths, are well-known features of spectra formed by prisms.   The corresponding equations for grating spectra (6.8 and 6.9) show that the dispersion depends on the grating interval $(a + b)$, being higher when this is finer, while the resolving power depends on the total number N of apertures producing interfering beams.   Both quantities depend directly on the order of the spectrum investigated. $\dfrac{d\theta}{d\lambda}$ is negative for a prism, since $\dfrac{d\mu}{d\lambda}$ is negative; this means that shorter wavelengths are more deviated.   It should also be noted that the grating dispersion formula 6.8 is applicable whatever the angle of incidence of the parallel light upon the grating.   This is so since it is equally well derived from the equation $(a + b)\,[\sin\theta + \sin i] = m\lambda$, which is the more general expression applicable when the angle of incidence is i.

Uniform dispersion (frequently spoken of as *normal dispersion*) occurs with a grating when the term $\cos\theta$ in equation 6.8 may be approximated as unity, i.e., when the diffracted light under observation lies within a range of angles near to the grating normal.

The above deductions do not allow for the finite breadth of the slit of the spectrometer in which the grating or the prism is used, nor for the imperfections of its optical system.   They are therefore valid only if the contributions to the breadth of the image (in monochromatic light) of the object slit, due to these causes, are small in comparison with those due to diffraction.   Poorer resolution is evidently obtained when the slit is too broad, or the aberration correction of the system insufficient.

CHAPTER 7

SOME ADDITIONAL ASPECTS OF OPTICAL IMAGE FORMATION

THE objects viewed by high-power microscopes are finely detailed, and usually need to be illuminated by condensing systems. Because of these facts, more complex considerations than those assumed earlier (on pp. 92–96) must be borne in mind for a real understanding of the operation of such instruments. An account is given here of image formation by an optical instrument when coherence conditions exist between neighbouring parts of the object. The discussion centres around the microscope as being the important case in which this arises. This, together with the earlier discussion in which the parts of objects were assumed completely incoherent, should provide a somewhat more complete picture of optical image formation in a variety of circumstances.

Effects of coherence between parts of the object were first studied by Abbe, and the following is essentially an account of the basic ideas of the Abbe theory of microscopic vision. The understanding of microscopic vision provided by this theory underlies some important techniques of microscopy, e.g., various methods of phase-contrast microscopy, some of quite recent introduction. These applications, along with other recently developed means of distinguishing object details, e.g., interference microscopes, are discussed briefly in the later parts of this chapter.

Abbe theory of microscopic vision

The expression $y = \dfrac{0 \cdot 61 \lambda}{\text{(N.A.)}}$ was obtained (on p. 95) for the resolving power of a microscope, assuming that the object points at distance y apart may be considered as entirely independent sources. The numerical aperture of a high-power (oil-immersion) microscope may be as much as $1 \cdot 5$, and substitution of this figure shows that distances of magnitude about $\lambda/2$ should be resolved if the above assumption is valid. Sources so near as this cannot, however, be completely incoherent, so that it is evidently necessary to discuss the effects likely to arise when phase relations exist between the emissions from the various parts of the object.

An object in the form of a single slit, illuminated from behind by parallel light, provides a simple example with which to commence such

103

a discussion. For a fixed direction of the incident light relative to the plane in which the slit lies, the relation between the phases of the emissions from the various points in the slit is constant. In the simple case when the light falls normally on the plane containing the slit, the emissions from all the points in the slit are in phase. Consider

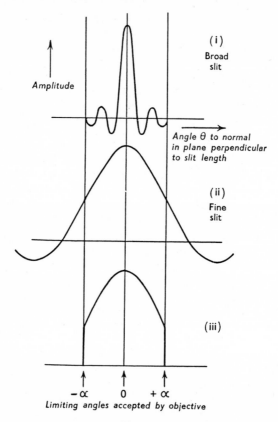

Fig. 7A.

this case, and let the direction of viewing of the microscope be perpendicular to the slit area, and the breadth of the slit symmetrically distributed about the microscope axis. Superposition of the waves from the various parts of the slit produces a resultant amplitude which varies with direction, having its maximum in the forward direction ($\theta = 0$, i.e., normal to the slit), and of the general form indicated in Fig. 7A (i). The reasons for this have been explained in Chapter 3. The angular spread of this diffraction pattern depends on the slit breadth, being smaller for broader slits.   Fig. 7A (i) and (ii) show the effects for a coarse and a finer slit.

The maximum inclination to the axis of light beams which can be accepted by the microscope is α, where $n \sin \alpha = $ N.A., so that it is possible that the whole of the diffracted light may not enter the microscope. The limits $+ \alpha$ and $- \alpha$ imposed by the aperture of the objective appear in Fig. 7A (i) and (ii).   In the first case almost all the diffracted light falls within these limits; in the other a considerable portion is not received by the instrument.   The essential idea of the Abbe treatment of resolution properties of microscopes is that the image is a progressively less faithful representation of the object the more the outer portions of the diffracted light are lost because of the aperture limitations of the instrument.   All the information about the object form is contained in the whole of the amplitude distribution with θ, but the objective may not receive all of this, and the image may be unrecognizable on this account.   For a particular numerical aperture a limit is set in this way to the fineness of an object which may be distinguished.   When the slit which gives the curve (ii) is viewed, the light actually accepted by the instrument varies in amplitude with direction in the manner indicated by Fig. 7A (iii).   The image seen will correspond to the object which would produce the diffraction pattern (iii).   This is evidently a more complicated object than the simple slit which produces the pattern (ii).   The criterion which determines the stage at which the essential features of the object are lost in the image is best discussed by reference to grating objects rather than to single slits.

Fig. 7B (i) shows the wave-optical aspects of the formation of the image of an object in the form of a grating illuminated normally from behind by parallel light, the diagram being simplified by imagining the refraction caused by the objective to occur entirely in the single plane AB.   The equivalent diagram from the standpoint of geometrical optics is shown in Fig. 7B (ii).

For purposes of explanation of the image formation in the terms of wave-optics, the action of the system may be considered in three stages.

First, the light incident upon the finely detailed object is *diffracted*. The intensity variation with angle to the axis of the system is given by the expression 3.3.   The main diffracted beams proceed in directions θ_m given by

$$d \sin \theta_m = m\lambda$$

where d is used for the grating interval $(a + b)$.   In Fig. 7B (i) two orders 1 and 2 are shown entering the objective in addition to the zero order 0. The first and second orders on the other side of the zero order, i.e., -1 and -2 (not shown), will also enter the objective.   Generally, some but not all of the diffracted beams enter the objective.

The diffracted beams which are incident within the correct range of directions are then *refracted* by the objective. The plane wave-fronts entering the instrument in various directions are altered in form by this process (see pp. 25–28) and, assuming the objective is aberration-free, converge towards points in its second focal plane after passing the objective. A series of images * 2, 1, 0, −1, −2, etc., corresponding to the various orders of diffraction is therefore produced in this plane.

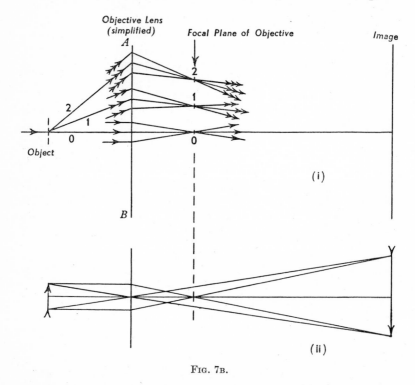

Fig. 7B.

It is important to note that since the deviation θ_m from the axis of the mth-order diffracted beam depends on the wavelength λ, the spacing of these images is different in the different wavelengths. The zero-order image is a white image, but the others are coloured, the short wavelengths being towards the zero-order image.

Confining attention at first to the effects in one wavelength, the third

* More generally, since the diffracted light is not entirely in the directions of the main diffracted beams, an amplitude pattern is formed in this plane. This pattern is accurately a Fourier transform of the amplitude pattern at the object plane only when the object is in the first focal plane of the objective lens. Otherwise it is only approximately so. See reference 28.

stage of the image formation is the effect of *interference* of all the beams emerging from the objective in regions where they all overlap, especially in the region some distance beyond the second focal plane of the objective. The image of the grating is an interference pattern due to these overlapping beams, which may be regarded as originating at the positions 0, 1, 2, etc., since these are real images and the beams pass on beyond them. In practice, the condensing system provides light in several directions, and a different set of diffracted images in the focal plane of the objective is produced for each direction of illumination of the object. Each of these produces interference fringes of the same spacing in the image plane, all of which superpose, producing the image of the grating. A distinct image occurs only in and near the image plane, since, elsewhere, the effect of all the overlapping beams is to cause loss of visibility of the fringes. Reduction of the range of directions of the light supplied by the condensing system increases the longitudinal range of image-plane positions upon which the image is reasonably distinct.

When white light is used, because of the variation with wavelength of the separation of the images 0, 1, 2, etc., the spacing of the fringes produced by the light passing on to the image is independent of wavelength. The image of the grating therefore appears as a series of un-coloured fringes, and the fringe spacing is the magnified grating interval.

The quality of the reproduction of the object form in the image depends on the passage, or otherwise, of the entire diffracted light through the objective. Imagine the actual lens in Fig. 7B (i) to be un-limited in aperture and the restrictions to the beams allowed to pass through the instrument to be caused by a stop placed in the second focal plane of the objective. Reduction in the size of this stop may interrupt the light focusing at 2, and its counterpart below the axis -2. Still further reduction would ultimately cut out 1 and -1, leaving only the zero order 0. It has been frequently shown in earlier parts of this book that the effect of using multiple interfering beams is to sharpen the fringes obtained. The distinctness of the reproduction of the fine grating object is therefore better the more sources such as 0, 1, 2, etc., contribute to the image, i.e., the wider the aperture. It is now neces-sary to ask how few of these images 0, 1, 2, etc., must remain un-interrupted if the essential feature of the object, i.e., its periodicity, is to be retained in its image. It is evident that transmission of the zero order alone could never give an indication of the nature of the object. No interference effects, such as are necessary to produce the fringe system which is the image of the grating, could be produced by the *single* beam passing on from the point 0. The passage of at least one order higher than zero is clearly necessary to give the first indication of the periodicity of the grating. With incident light parallel to the axis, and an aperture which is circular round the axis, the admission of one first-order diffracted spectrum (Fig. 7B(i) (1)) involves admission of that on the other side of the axis (-1) also, so that both these spectra contribute to the image, together with the zero order. This case will be considered first, though it will be seen later that it is possible to improve on the resolution obtained in this way by providing light in directions inclined to the normal to the object.

Assuming λ_0 is the wavelength in the object space (refractive index n) corresponding to the wavelength λ *in vacuo*, then $n\lambda_0 = \lambda$. The first-order spectrum for the grating object, of interval d, occurs in the direction θ_1 to the axis, such that

$$\lambda_0 = d \sin \theta_1$$

or,
$$\sin \theta_1 = \frac{\lambda}{nd}$$

Using α again for the semi-angular aperture in the object space, resolution will be obtained provided

$$\alpha \geqslant \theta_1$$

or
$$\sin \alpha \geqslant \frac{\lambda}{nd}$$

or
$$d \geqslant \frac{\lambda}{\text{N.A.}} \quad . \quad . \quad . \quad . \quad . \quad \textbf{7.1}$$

A finer limit of resolution is, however, possible if incident light is provided in more suitable directions, in particular if it is provided in

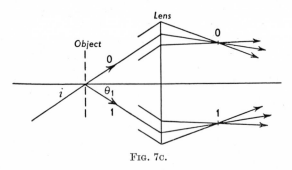

FIG. 7C.

such a direction that the zero order and one only of the first-order images are just admitted. This case is illustrated in its essentials in Fig. 7C. The zero and first-order images of the illuminating source are evidently symmetrically disposed about the axis of the instrument when i, the angle of incidence of the light upon the grating, is equal to θ_1.

The grating formula for non-normal incidence and first-order diffraction is

$$(\sin i + \sin \theta_1) = \frac{\lambda_0}{d} = \frac{\lambda}{nd}$$

or, when

$$i = \theta_1,$$

$$\sin \theta_1 = \frac{\lambda}{2nd}$$

The images 0 and 1 will be admitted, and resolution obtained, when

$$\alpha \geqslant \theta_1$$

or

$$d \geqslant \frac{\lambda}{2\text{N.A.}} \quad . \quad . \quad . \quad . \quad . \quad . \quad \textbf{7.2}$$

To obtain full benefit of this optimum resolution light must be provided in directions which include the value $i = \theta_1$, so that the condition $i = \theta_1$ for the finest resolvable detail may be realized,   In other words, the condenser must supply a convergent cone of light having a semi-angle not less than the semi-angular aperture of the objective.   A condenser with an annular aperture, producing rays of a more restricted range of inclinations to the axis (including the value α), would also allow the limits of detail to be viewed satisfactorily.

Experimental verifications of the conclusions reached above are possible using grating objects with various illumination arrangements. A variable aperture inserted in the second focal plane of the objective permits control of the aperture to a measureable extent.   If this is done until the periodic appearance of the image of a grating is just no longer distinguishable, agreement is found between the experimentally measured aperture and the value expected from the Abbe theory. Abbe himself performed several experiments of this type in the development of his theory.

The objects viewed by microscopes do not normally consist of regularly spaced gratings of the type so far discussed, but the theory is nevertheless applicable to objects of a more general type.   This was made clear by Johnstone Stoney (1896), who showed that any *amplitude object* (i.e., an object of such a kind that the amplitude of the light leaving the object in the direction of the instrument varies from point to point over the object) corresponds in effect to the superposed effects of the apertures of a large number of gratings varying in fineness and orientation.   Each of these gratings is reproduced in the image plane in the manner described above, and the finest grating spacing for which this can occur is given by equation 7.2, so that this expression still indicates the magnitude of the smallest resolvable details in the object.

Phase objects and dark-ground illumination

Many objects of the kind which it is desirable to examine by microscope are of a different type from those so far described, being almost equally transparent but varying in refractive index, and hence in optical thickness, over their area.   When such an object is illuminated from behind the light varies over the object area in phase rather than in amplitude as it leaves the object in the direction of the instrument.   Such an object is known as a *phase object*.

The distribution over the image area of the amplitudes and phases of the light arriving there may be expected to correspond exactly * to that which exists as the light leaves the object, provided the instrument is optically perfect and collects all the light diffracted by the object.   Since the illumination at any point in the image plane depends only on the square of the amplitude, this would be uniform over the image under these conditions if a pure phase object were used.   The details of the object would not be visible in the image.   It is therefore necessary to consider possible methods of converting the phase modulation at the object into corresponding amplitude modulation at the image, and thus to render visible the phase details of the object. Some methods for achieving this have been in use for many years. The object structure is not, however, always easily inferred in detail from the image viewed when these methods are used.   The recently introduced phase-contrast method produces image-brightness variations which correspond fairly closely to the object-phase variations, and is especially applicable to smaller ranges of phase than can be rendered visible by the older methods.   The older methods are described briefly first; the next section describes the principles of phase-contrast microscopy.

If the optical system used for viewing the phase-object has residual aberrations, the optical paths between any pair of conjugate object and image points are not all equal.   The waves of various amplitudes and phases diffracted in various directions at the object recombine in the image plane; and, because of this inconstant optical path, they do so in rather different ways at different positions in the image.   The constant amplitude over the image, which would arise with an aberrationless system, no longer occurs, and indications of the presence of the object in the form of intensity variations over the image plane are then to be expected.   Residual aberration of the microscope objective may therefore result in intensity effects which depend on the object structure.   With normal good-quality microscope objectives adjustment so that the instrument is slightly out of focus can cause an object with mainly phase-structure to " appear "; this evidently depends in

* This is known as the theorem of Lummer.

a similar way upon the existence of a range of optical paths from object to image points, deliberately introduced in this case by the out-of-focus adjustment. Reduction of the angular aperture of the condensing system contributes to a clearer representation of the phase-structure of the object, when the method of out of focus adjustment is used. The effect of reduction of the range of directions of the light falling upon the object, mentioned on p. 107, is partly responsible for this.

Other methods depend on the use of an arrangement of condensing and objective lenses such that the light diffracted by the object is not entirely collected by the objective. The most notable of these is the method of *dark-ground illumination*, the essentials of which are indicated in Fig. 7D. The objective of the microscope accepts light within

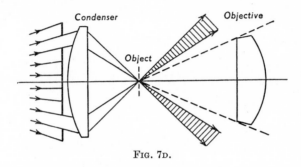

FIG. 7D.

the range indicated by the dotted lines, which does not include any of the incident-light directions.

The principles of the method of dark-ground illumination, and also of the phase-contrast method which is described later, are clarified by the following discussion (after Zernicke), which shows that any *relative* changes, of either phase or amplitude, introduced into the beams diffracted in the various directions by the phase object under examination, can result in intensity modulation of the image. This is done in the method of dark-ground illumination by eliminating the amplitude contributions at the image due to the zero-order diffracted beams (these beams are not accepted by the objective), while the higher-order diffracted beams are accepted without modification. In Fig. 7E a phase object illuminated by light parallel to the axis of the instrument is represented. Beyond the object the passage through the (simplified) objective of the undeviated or zero-order portion of the light beam only is shown. Consider the phase-object as made up of a large number n elements of equal area, some of which, numbered 1 to 6, appear in the diagram. The light emerging from the object areas 1 to 6 is represented in amplitude and phase by the corresponding lines CP_1 to CP_6 in Fig.

7F. If the entire diffracted light is accepted by the objective, and the latter is assumed aberration-free, the relative amplitudes and phases of the light arriving at the image areas 1 to 6 are the same as those existing

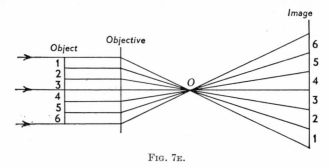

FIG. 7E.

as the light leaves the corresponding object areas.* Fig. 7F therefore also represents the phases and amplitudes of the light arriving at the various elements of the image in these circumstances. For a pure phase object the amplitudes CP_1 to CP_6, etc., are equal and the points

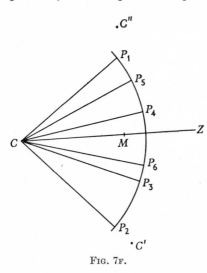

FIG. 7F.

P_1 to P_6, etc., lie on a circle around C; and the intensity, depending only on the magnitude of the amplitude, is the same everywhere over the image. It is necessary next to consider the effect of incomplete transmission of the diffracted beams by the objective; and, in the case of dark-ground illumination, the effect of removal of the direct light is of main interest. Fig. 7E shows only this direct light passing through the instrument, and the amplitude and phase of this light at any of the elemental areas of the image may be determined in the following way. The n zero-order plane waves, emerging from the various object elements, superpose at O (Fig. 7E) after being refracted by the objective. The effect at O, and at any constant distance beyond O, is therefore a vectorial summation of all the waves having the ranges of phases indicated by Fig. 7F. If the direction CZ

* This is true no matter what the direction of the incident light upon the object, and the conclusions are applicable in the more general case of oblique illumination.

indicates the mean phase, it is clear that the summation of all the vectors such as CP_1, CP_2, etc., gives a vector in the direction CZ and of length $(n \times CM)$, where M is the centroid of the n points such as P_1, P_2 . . . etc. In the image plane this zero-order light is spread over n elements of area, so that the amplitude and phase of the zero-order light is indicated by the line CM for each element.

There remains to be considered the effect of removing this contribution to the total light at each element of image area. Confining attention to one of these elements, say 1, the line CP_1 in Fig. 7F represents the amplitude and phase of the total light received there, while CM represents the contribution to this of the direct light only. Since CM and MP_1 give CP_1 by vectorial addition, the effect after removal of the direct light is indicated in amplitude and phase by the length and direction of MP_1. Hence removal of the direct light corresponds to shift of the origin in Fig. 7F from C to M. The lines MP_1 to MP_6, etc., of various lengths, correspond to the amplitudes at the image areas 1 to 6, etc., and their squares to the intensities there. Uneven intensity variation with phase is evidently obtained, the variation being undesirably rapid for phases near the mean value. Also areas where the phases are either advanced or retarded relative to the mean phase are increased in brightness compared with those nearer the mean. For example, the areas 5 and 3, whose phases are equally distributed about the mean, have equal values for MP_5 and MP_3, and hence are equally illuminated. The method of dark-ground illumination, while permitting a representation of the object to be viewed, produces results which need very careful interpretation, and the rapid intensity variation with phase is an undesirable feature in the images obtained.

Phase-contrast microscopy

In the method of phase-contrast microscopy the beams of various order diffracted by the object all contribute to the image, but these are changed in relative phase by the insertion of a suitably arranged phaseplate in the second focal plane of the objective. This is illustrated in Fig. 7G. An annular ring restricts the condenser aperture so that light within a small range of inclinations to the axis falls upon the object. Beyond the object the direction limits of the direct light and of the diffracted light are indicated. Mounted in the second focal plane of the objective is a uniform transparent sheet on which is deposited a thin annular ring of material such as cryolite in such a position that the direct light only must pass through it. The direct light is thus retarded in phase by an amount dependent on the thickness of this annular film. This is usually chosen so that the phase retardation is about 90°. The effect of this may be discussed by reference to Fig. 7F again. Suppose phase retardation to be represented in that figure by anti-clockwise rotation of the vectors such as CP_1, etc. It was shown in the previous section that the amplitude and phase of light arriving at any elemental image area, such as 1, was represented by the length and direction of CP_1; and that this could be regarded as the vectorial sum of CM, the contribution due to the direct light, and MP_1, that due to the indirect light. Supposing now that the direct light is retarded in phase by 90°, this is equivalent to turning CM through a right angle in an anti-clockwise direction about either C or M. $C'M$ in the figure therefore represents the direct light in these circumstances. The resultant of this and MP_1 now represents the amplitude at the area 1. This is clearly $C'P_1$. The amplitudes corre-

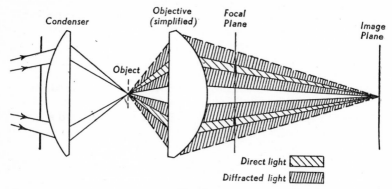

Fig. 7G.

sponding to the various object elements 1 to 6, etc., are indicated by the situations of the corresponding points P_1 to P_6, etc., relative to a new origin at C'. It is clear that the more phase-retarding object elements appear brighter, and a much smoother variation of intensity with phase is obtained.

If the direct light is advanced in phase by 90° relative to the indirect light (by depositing the cryolite film on the whole of the plate in the objective focal plane, except for the annulus through which the direct light passes) the effect is to move the origin to C'' (Fig. 7F), and the greater the retardation of phase, the darker the corresponding image area. This is known as negative phase contrast.

Interference microscopes

Consider the effect of supplementing the light passing in some direction through part of a phase object by a further beam of light of the same amplitude; let the second beam be ultimately in the same direction as the first, and both beams received by a microscope focused upon the object. Interference between these beams will occur, and the resultant amplitude at the image region, corresponding to the portion of the object concerned, will depend on the phase difference between the two beams. This in turn depends on the phase retardation of the first beam as it passes through the object. The image formed by monochromatic light should therefore appear covered with interference fringes, each of which represents a locus of constant phase in the object, consecutive fringes corresponding to portions of the object where the phase differs by 2π. If only finer phase variations than this exist in the object, intensity changes dependent on these phase changes will be evident in the image plane. With white light, variations in colour over the image plane should appear.

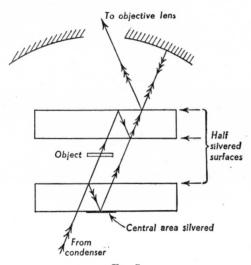

To objective lens

Half silvered surfaces

Object

Central area silvered

From condenser

FIG. 7H.

Several interference microscopes have been designed, mostly making use of the principle outlined above, using either double-beam or multiple-beam interference. A summary of these is given in reference 19 in the bibliography. The Dyson interference microscope will be described as an example which puts into practice the above-mentioned principles in a simple and effective way. The part of this instrument of essential interest is the arrangement for supplying to the microscope two superposed coherent beams, only one of which has passed through the object. This is done in the manner illustrated in Fig. 7H. It is evident that the operation of such an arrangement is similar in principle to that of interference refractometers described in the next chapter. Dyson has also devised an arrangement for microscopic examination of details of opaque metallic surfaces, based on the same principles.

CHAPTER 8

INSTRUMENTAL APPLICATIONS OF INTERFERENCE AND DIFFRACTION

1. *INTERFEROMETERS*

SEVERAL instruments of the interferometer type are described in the present chapter, together with the main applications of these instruments. In many cases the treatment is brief, being confined to the general arrangement and principles of action of the instrument concerned. The reader is referred to fuller accounts of interferometry in the bibliography (see e.g., references 2, 15, 16).

The Rayleigh and Jamin interferometers

The Rayleigh interferometer consists essentially of the arrangement shown in Fig. 8A (i) and (ii). The lenses L_1 and L_2 are achromatic

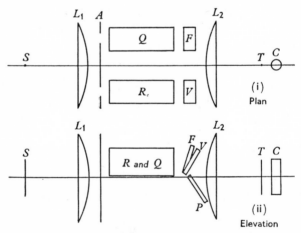

FIG. 8A.

doublets which are well corrected for spherical aberration also. The object slit S, in the first focal plane of L_1, would, in the absence of any intervening apertures, produce a sharp image at T in the second focal plane of L_2. Insertion of a double slit at A produces a Fraunhofer diffraction pattern around T in this focal plane, of the form indicated by equation 3.2. The interference features of this pattern are produced

116

in precisely the same way as in Young's original double-slit experiment. The beams emerging from the separated slits pass through similar plane-ended chambers Q and R before being refracted by the lens L_2, and the optical paths of the beams may be altered by alteration of the gas pressure in either of these chambers.   Considerably separated slits must evidently be used (about 1 inch separation is usual), and as a result the fringe separation is exceedingly small.   A very fine object slit S must therefore be used so that serious loss of distinctness of the fringes may not arise because of relative displacement of the parts of the fringe system due to the various parts of the slit breadth.   The fringes are so fine that a very high-power eyepiece C must be used to increase their apparent separation and so to render them visible.   The amount of light available from the narrow slit is so limited that a normal eyepiece of sufficient power would reduce the intensity of the enlarged fringe system to an impossibly low value.   Magnification in the direction perpendicular to the fringes only is required, and this is achieved by using a cylindrical glass tube (of a few millimetres diameter),

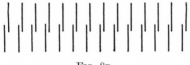

Fig. 8b.

the axis being parallel to the slit S.   Dimensions in the fringe system parallel to the fringes are not magnified, so that reduction of illumination due to this cause is eliminated.

It is not possible to insert a cross-hair at T, since the finest hair would be very broad and irregular relative to the fringe breadth.   A second set of similar fringes is used as a fiduciary system.   The beams from the apertures at A also pass under the tubes R and Q (see Fig. 8a (ii)) and are then thrown upwards slightly before entering the lens L_2, by means of an inclined parallel-sided plate P arranged as shown. A system of fringes such as is illustrated in Fig. 8b is therefore seen, the lower fringes being fixed and the upper ones capable of transverse movement as the refractive index in R or Q is altered.   If the refractive indices in R and Q are n_R and n_Q and the length of the chambers is l cm., the optical-path difference is $(n_R - n_Q)l$ cm. and the upper fringes are shifted with respect to the lower ones by m times the fringe separation, m being such that

$$(n_R - n_Q)l = m\lambda \quad . \quad . \quad . \quad . \quad . \quad \textbf{8.1}$$

If both R and Q are first evacuated, and a gas then allowed to leak slowly into R, the movement of the fringes may be seen and the quantity

m observed, so that n_R at any pressure is determinable. Observations of m may be made to about $\frac{1}{40}$th of an order. The smallest detectable difference in n is therefore obtained by substitution of $m = \frac{1}{40}$ in equation 8.1.

In practice it is common to use an arrangement which compensates for the path difference, in such a way that no relative movement of the fringe systems occurs. This is done by means of two parallel-sided glass plates F and V (Fig. 8A), one in each of the beams issuing from the chambers R and Q. These are inclined to the beams, one (F) being fixed in inclination, and the other (V) being variable. If n_R, for instance, increases, the increased optical length of the beam through R may be compensated for by reduction of the inclination of V to the beam. A micrometer measures very small changes in inclination of

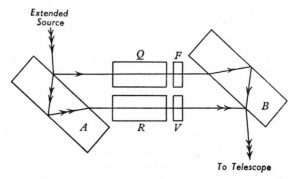

Fig. 8c.

V, and its reading when the upper fringes are unaltered in displacement gives the refractive-index difference between R and Q. White light may be used to ascertain that the zero-order fringes do really correspond both before and after any difference is made in the refractive index in R and Q. This is especially necessary if a non-progressive change in the value of n_R is to be measured, e.g., if the small difference between the refractive indices of a pure and impure liquid is to be found. In such a case the fringes cannot be kept constantly undisplaced by use of the compensating arrangement during the change.

The *Jamin interferometer* effects the separation of the two interfering beams, and recombines them to form fringes, in a different way, but the principles of its use as a refractometer are similar to those of the Rayleigh instrument. This instrument was developed in 1856, and for some time thereafter was the only instrument available for refractive index measurements by interferometric means. Fig. 8c shows the essential arrangement in plan. The thick glass plates A and

B are of similar thickness, and each has parallel optically flat surfaces. The beams following the two courses shown superpose, and if one of the plates is slightly tilted about a horizontal axis parallel to its plane, horizontal fringes of equal inclination are seen in the telescope viewing the recombined beams.   The fringes are produced in the same way as Brewster fringes.   They are broader than those obtained with the Rayleigh instrument, and a cross-wire may be used in this case.   A compensating arrangement is again employed; usually of a type such that F and V both rotate about a common axis.   These plates are mounted so that increase of the inclination of the light upon one plate is accompanied by decrease of inclination upon the other, so that rotation increases the optical path in one beam and reduces it in the other.

As a brief appendage to this section the *Michelson stellar interferometer* may be described, since its principles are similar to those of the Rayleigh interferometer.   Omitting the gas or liquid chambers from the latter interferometer, the essential arrangement is a double slit,

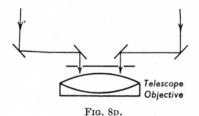

Telescope
Objective

FIG. 8D.

illuminated by parallel light, and a telescopic viewing arrangement. If two parallel beams at a small angular separation ϕ both illuminate the double slit, then two interference fringe patterns appear in the focal plane of the telescope objective (focal length f), their relative displacement being $f\phi$.   If d is the slit separation, the linear separation of the interference maxima in each of the diffracted patterns is $f \cdot \dfrac{\lambda}{d}$. Hence the fringes due to the two illuminating beams will just superpose if $\phi = 0$, $\dfrac{\lambda}{d}$, $\dfrac{2\lambda}{d}$, etc.   They will be just out of step for the ϕ values exactly intermediate between these.   If d may be adjusted, and is increased from low values, the first position at which the fringes are just out of step is such that $\phi = \dfrac{\lambda}{2d}$.   A means is thus available of determining angular separations of distant objects, such as stars, and the idea may be extended to determination of diameters of circular sources such as single stars.   The distance d required is very large, and a system of mirrors as indicated in Fig. 8D was used by Michelson in his stellar interferometer. The outer mirrors acted as the separated slits, selecting limited portions of the broad incident wave-fronts, which were ultimately admitted to the telescope in the manner shown.

The Michelson interferometer

The interferometer designed by Michelson (Fig. 8E) is essentially a thin-film interference device, in which the interfering beams are well separated over considerable portions of their courses. The plate P is arranged at 45° to the incident light direction. It is silvered on the surface Q so that the reflected and transmitted portions of the beam arriving there are about equal. These portions fall normally on the plane mirrors M_1 and M_2 and return again to Q. The portions of these

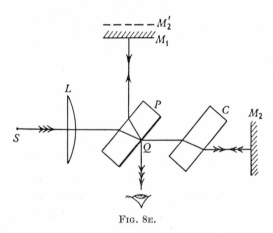

FIG. 8E.

then proceeding in the direction of the eye are about equal. The mirrors are plane to a high degree of accuracy; one (M_1) is fixed, while the other may be moved very slowly in the direction perpendicular to its plane, and its movement measured with high precision. The plates C and P are two parts of one original plate with accurately parallel optically flat surfaces; C is known as the compensating plate, and is inserted in order that each of the interfering beams may pass through three identical thicknesses of glass; any path difference between the beams is thus entirely due to the situation of M_2. The plate C may also be used to effect small changes in the path of the beam reflected at M_2 by slight alteration of its tilt.

The beam entering the eye from M_2 may clearly be considered as coming from the virtual image of M_2 in the surface Q. This is indicated by the dotted line M_2' in Fig. 8E. The fringes seen are therefore the same as would be produced by the thin-film arrangement having surfaces M_1 and M_2'. Slight alteration of the tilt of one of the mirrors, so that the light falls not quite perpendicularly upon it, gives wedge fringes situated in the vicinity of the wedge when parallel light is incident on the interferometer. White-light fringes may be viewed when the paths are equal, i.e., when M_1 and M_2' intersect. The zero-order fringe will be along the line of intersection of M_1 and M_2'.

When M_1 and M_2' are accurately parallel, circular fringes may be seen if convergent light is used. These are the normal fringes of con-stant inclination obtainable with a parallel-sided thin film. They are localized at infinity, and a telescopic arrangement is necessary for viewing them.

The Michelson interferometer is a double-beam interferometer, and the intensity variation in the fringes is of the normal $\cos^2\gamma$ type. The lack of sharpness of the intensity maxima means that it is considerably inferior to the Fabry–Pérot interferometer in most respects. Interest in the instrument in its original form is now mainly of a historical kind.

Refractive-index measurements are possible with a Michelson inter-ferometer, introducing an evacuated chamber into one beam and a chamber containing the gas or other medium into the other; the method is in principle precisely similar to that used with Rayleigh and Jamin refractometers. Wavelength measurements are possible with an instrument of this type, by counting fringes as the mirror M_2 is moved over a known distance. The determination of the length of the standard metre in terms of the cadmium 6438 Å wavelength, performed by Michelson and Benoit (1895), was an experiment of this nature using the instrument to the limit of its capabilities. Similar methods have been used by later observers using Fabry–Pérot etalons and in-troducing other refinements; the methods do not differ in principle from the original determination, and a later section is devoted to a discussion of these.

Michelson also applied his interferometer to investigations into the structure of spectral lines. A simple example will illustrate the ideas underlying such investigations. Suppose a spectral line is really a doublet, consisting of wavelengths λ and $\lambda + \Delta\lambda$. If light of this nature is used to illuminate a thin film in the form of an air-wedge, the condition for maximum reinforcement where the wedge thickness is e is $2e = (m + \frac{1}{2})\lambda$.* For the wavelength $\lambda + \Delta\lambda$ the order of inter-ference will be different by Δm at this point in the wedge. Differentia-tion yields

$$\frac{\Delta m}{(m + \frac{1}{2})} = -\frac{\Delta\lambda}{\lambda}$$

* In the Michelson interferometer the change of phase effects are not the same as in a wedge, because of the use of silvered surfaces, and the reinforcement con-dition is $2e = m\lambda$. This does not affect the above argument.

If $\Delta m = \frac{1}{2}, \frac{3}{2}$, etc., the maxima of one fringe system will coincide with the minima of the other, and the contrast between the brights and darks in the interference pattern will be lost. Least distinctness of the fringes will therefore occur at e values such that $(m + \frac{1}{2})$ is $\frac{1}{2}\dfrac{\lambda}{\Delta\lambda}$, $\frac{3}{2}\dfrac{\lambda}{\Delta\lambda}$, ... etc. The actual values of e are $\dfrac{\lambda^2}{4\Delta\lambda}, \dfrac{3\lambda^2}{4\Delta\lambda}$, ... etc. The wedge thicknesses intermediate between these values correspond to $\Delta m = 1, 2$, etc., so that the maxima in the two-fringe system superpose exactly for these values of e, giving very distinct fringes.

The alternate thickness positions where the fringes are distinct and indistinct may easily be observed using sodium illumination (wavelength components 5890 and 5896 Å) upon a wedge of angle about 30' and several centimetres in length. The corresponding experiment with a Michelson interferometer involves steadily moving M_2 and noting its position when maximum and minimum distinctness occurs. The distance between consecutive positions of the same sort allows a value of $\Delta\lambda$ to be found.

The more general problem consists in determining the shapes of single lines (i.e., their intensity variation with wavelength) from the fringe appearance for successive adjustments of M_2. Michelson developed methods for doing this for some symmetrical spectral lines. The range of wavelengths in spectral lines leads ultimately to confusion of the fringe system at high orders, and is one of the reasons for the upper limits to the thickness e of films which will give observable fringes. The Cd 6438 Å was chosen for the metre-standardization experiments because of its extreme sharpness, enabling very considerable path differences to be estimated. Krypton and mercury-isotope sources have recently been developed which are still more suitable in this respect.

The Fabry–Pérot interferometer

The Fabry–Pérot interferometer consists of two glass plates with high-quality optically-flat surfaces, coated on the nearest faces with high-reflecting films. The two plates may be adjusted to be parallel, and their separation is variable without loss of parallelism by movement of one of them. Precise measurement of the movement of the variable plate is possible. Circular fringes of constant inclination may be viewed using convergent light symmetrical around an axis perpendicular to the plates. For some applications one plate may be slightly tilted and equal optical-thickness fringes viewed using parallel illumination. The sharpness of the bright fringes, which results from the use of parallel silvered faces, is, however, retained with wedge fringes only when the wedge thicknesses are small. Path differences of several centimetres may be used with constant inclination fringes, and hence very high orders of interference may be examined. It is evident that, because of the sharpness of the fringes obtained with high-reflecting surfaces, fractions of orders are estimated with high accuracy, and comparisons between wavelengths can be made to a high degree of precision. Very close wavelengths may be distinguished, the performance in this respect evidently increasing with the order of interference and the fineness of the maxima in any wavelength. These factors are in turn dependent on the separation of the plates and the reflecting power of the surface coatings.

Estimation of the resolving limit of an interferometer of this type may be made using equation 5.4, which describes the form of the interference maxima, and applying the Rayleigh criterion for resolution in a rather different way than has previously been employed. The Rayleigh resolution condition, as hitherto stated, is that the central maxima of intensity distributions in two wavelengths must not be nearer than the half-width of one of these. For Fraunhofer diffraction patterns formed by single apertures, gratings, etc., this half-width is the distance from the position of maximum intensity to the first zero on one side of it. The Fabry–Pérot fringe intensities are such that the intensity does not fall to zero and rise again close to the maximum, but falls off sharply and then more slowly, only reaching a low value at quite a large distance from the fringe centre (see Fig. 5H). The Rayleigh criterion, defined in the above way, loses its meaning in this case. If, however, it is stated in such a form that the intensity I at the points of overlap must not exceed a certain fraction of the central intensity I_0 in each distribution, it may be applied also to Fabry–Pérot fringes, while still retaining the same meaning in other cases. Expressed in this way, the Rayleigh criterion takes the form

$$I \leqslant 0 \cdot 405 I_0$$

This is illustrated in Fig. 8F, which shows maxima of the same order m in wavelengths λ and $\lambda + \Delta\lambda$, which are just resolved according to the Rayleigh criterion.*

Substitution of $I/I_0 = 0 \cdot 405$ into equation 5.4 yields

$$\delta = 2 \sin^{-1}\left[\pm \frac{0 \cdot 606(1 - r^2)}{r}\right] = 2(m\pi \pm \alpha)$$

where α is the smallest angle having its sine equal to $\dfrac{0 \cdot 606(1 - r^2)}{r}$.

* When wavelengths of unequal intensity are concerned, the closest separation depends on the relative intensities, and no single statement of the limit suffices for all cases. $I \leqslant 0 \cdot 405 I_0$ may still be used as an indication of the resolution limit, where I_0 is the intensity of the weaker line. Greater separation of the lines is evidently necessary for resolution when the intensities are unequal.

The maxima occur at δ values $2m\pi$, where m, the order of interference, has all possible integral values. Departure of δ from integral multiples of 2π by $\pm 2\alpha$ reduces the intensity from I_0 to $0\cdot405I_0$. Since a change in δ by 2π corresponds to unit change in order, a difference 2α in δ corresponds to a difference in order of $\dfrac{\alpha}{\pi}$. The wavelengths λ and $\lambda + \Delta\lambda$, which are just resolved, correspond in separation to a difference in

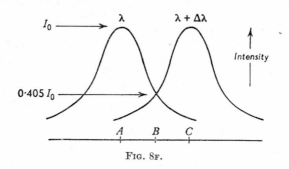

FIG. 8F.

order Δm equal to twice this amount, since the distance AC (Fig. 8F) is twice AB. Thus Δm, corresponding to the minimum resolvable wavelength difference $\Delta\lambda$, is $\dfrac{2\alpha}{\pi}$.

Now since $m\lambda$ is constant for any fixed angle of incidence (equal to $2e$ for normal incidence), differentiation yields

$$m \cdot \Delta\lambda + \lambda \cdot \Delta m = 0$$

or
$$\frac{\lambda}{\Delta\lambda} = -\frac{m}{\Delta m}$$

The negative sign indicates that wavelength increase corresponds to a decrease in order of interference.

The resolving power is therefore given by

$$\frac{\lambda}{\Delta\lambda} = \frac{m\pi}{2 \sin^{-1}\left[\dfrac{0\cdot606(1 - r^2)}{r}\right]} \qquad \cdots \qquad 8.1$$

Since $k\lambda$ is constant (equal to unity), where k is the wave-number, $\Delta k = -k\dfrac{\Delta\lambda}{\lambda}$. This minimum wave-number resolvable, equal to the wave-number divided by the resolving power, is of more immediately obvious meaning and is often quoted in connection with high-resolution instruments, being frequently termed the *resolving limit*.

Equation 8.1 indicates how the resolution is improved by using higher interference orders, and also by increasing the reflecting power r^2 of the surfaces. It may easily be shown from this equation that an increase of r^2 from 0·5 to 0·9 increases the resolving power about seven-fold. The resolving limit at 5000 Å in the best conditions is about 0·0025 cm.$^{-1}$.

One of the advantages of the Fabry–Pérot interferometer with variable plate separation is that ambiguities in the interpretation of the results obtained may be resolved by repetition with different plate separations. Interferometers of the same type with fixed plate spacings are known as *Fabry–Pérot etalons*, and a selection of two or three etalons having spacings in the range 0·5–5·0 cm. is useful for a wide range of spectroscopic work. The manner in which Fabry–Pérot etalons are employed in high-resolution spectroscopy is indicated along with other high-resolution procedures later in this chapter. It is evidently possible to determine length accurately by the use of Fabry–Pérot fringes. In principle this may be done by moving one plate over the length concerned and determining by counting of fringes the change in order at some point in the field of view. The next section outlines methods of length measurement which are developments of this principle.

Interferometric measurement of length standards

Up to 1940 nine determinations of the length of the international metre in terms of the Cd 6438 Å wavelength had been made. The methods of the two earliest determinations, together with that of Sears and Barrell, which may be taken as representative of the later developments, will be discussed. The results obtained in these experiments are as follows:

Michelson and Benoit	.	. 1895	6438·4691Å
Benoit, Fabry, and Pérot	.	1906	6438·4703Å
Sears and Barrell	.	. 1934	6438·4709Å

The methods employed in these determinations are all similar in principle, the later experiments involving only refinements in procedure. In each determination a sequence of etalons, having lengths related as nearly as possible in a simple numerical way, was used. The three stages of procedure were:

(i) Determination of the length of the shortest etalon in terms of the chosen light wavelength.

(ii) Intercomparison of the etalons.

(iii) Comparison of the longest etalon with the standard metre.

The first stage of the procedure is a particular example of the general problem of length measurement in terms of light wavelengths,

E

and the methods described therefore also illustrate wider applications, such as accurate measurement of mechanical gauge lengths.

(i) In the first experiment of this kind Michelson and Benoit used nine etalons of lengths ranging from about 0·39 mm. to 10 cm., the ratio of lengths of successive etalons in the series being closely two to one. In addition to being spaced apart longitudinally, the etalon mirrors were displaced laterally, so that when an etalon was placed with its mirrors perpendicular to one beam of the Michelson interferometer, two portions of this beam were reflected from the two mirrors. White-light fringes could be viewed in the part of the field corresponding to one or the other of these two mirrors when the movable mirror in the other beam was suitably adjusted. Moving this mirror over the range defined by these limits was therefore equivalent to movement over the etalon length. Counting of fringes in Cd 6438 Å light during this motion, with careful estimation of the fraction by which the number exceeded an integral value, therefore led to the relation between the shortest etalon and this wavelength. The number of fringes observed was 1212·37. The large number of fringes involved, for even a short etalon, illustrates the limits of such a procedure.

A further method which uses several wavelengths, known as the *method of exact fractions*, was developed by Benoit. This has the advantage that it is not necessary to count large numbers of fringes. The principle of this method will be illustrated first by an example in which simple numbers are chosen, the magnitudes being also entirely different from those arising in the actual optical problem. Suppose three standards of length A, B, and C have magnitudes closely equal to 2·3, 3·1, and 4·2 cm. Another unknown length D is known in some way to be related to A, B, and C as follows:

$$D = (m_1 + 0·8_5)A = (m_2 + 0·1_0)B = (m_3 + 0·7_5)C$$

where m_1, m_2, and m_3 are unknown integers and the fractions are known to within, say, 0·05.

It is evident that this information enables D to be determined, by trial with possible integral values of m_1, m_2, and m_3, until a suitable combination is obtained giving D values which agree. This occurs in the simple example cited when $m_1 = 6$, $m_2 = 5$, $m_3 = 3$, giving $D = 15·8$ cm. The essential point is that the fractions remaining when D is measured in terms of the respective standards A, B, and C determine a limited number of possible values of D.

In the optical problem D corresponds to twice the etalon separation, while A, B, and C are three considerably different wavelengths, known to sufficient accuracy by other means. The orders of interference in these wavelengths (corresponding to the etalon spacing) are not known, but the fraction by which some integral value is exceeded is in each case determinable quite closely, especially if very fine Fabry–Pérot fringes are under observation.   The linear plot of $\cos \phi_m$ with m is extrapolated to $\cos \phi = 1$, so giving the fraction by which the order corresponding to the perpendicular separation of the etalon plates exceeds an integral value.   The etalon separation should, in principle, be determinable from these fractions.   In practice, it is necessary to have some guidance regarding the ranges of the whole numbers m_1, m_2, and m_3 in which the trial-and-error procedure is to be followed, since each of these numbers is very large.   This guidance is obtained from a less precise knowledge of the etalon separation by other means, e.g., by use of a travelling microscope.   The usual procedure in the calculation is to determine first the range of possible m_1 values corresponding to the D value of limited accuracy known in this way.   Then each of these hypothetical orders for the wavelength A is taken in turn, together with the known fraction which goes with it, and the corresponding possible etalon lengths determined.   The orders (and their fractions) of the other two wavelengths which would correspond to these lengths are then determined.   Except in the case of the one correct m_1 value, the fractions by which the orders in wavelengths B and C exceed the whole numbers m_2 and m_3 do not correspond correctly with the known fractions.   The correct integral values of m_1, m_2, and m_3 are therefore found in this way.

For the very high values of m_1, m_2, m_3 involved, more than one combination of three integral numbers may give D values which agree.   It is necessary therefore that the independent measurement of D should give its value sufficiently closely to eliminate all but one of the possible combinations, so that the result may be free from ambiguity.   In cases where it is not possible to obtain the coarser measure of D with sufficient closeness to achieve this, repetition with a fourth or even a fifth wavelength may reveal significant differences in the fractions in all but the correct case.   An example of a representative calculation is given in reference 21.

(ii) Following the determination of the length l_1, of the shortest etalon as a multiple of the Cd wavelength, the next stage in procedure in each of these experiments was the intercomparison of the etalons. In all the methods except that used by Sears and Barrell, the consecutive etalons had lengths as nearly as possible in the ratio $2 : 1$. The length l_2 of the second etalon was determined as a multiple of the standard wavelength, by finding the number of fringes corresponding to the small difference between l_2 and $2l_1$.   In the Michelson experiment this was done by placing the two etalons side by side so that their two front mirrors were exactly abreast, which was known to be the case by obtaining white-light fringes in the parts of the field of the Michelson interferometer corresponding to both mirrors.   The shorter etalon was then moved back through its own length, which was done by first obtaining white-light fringes in its rear mirror and then moving it back until later they appeared in the front mirror. The rear mirrors of the two etalons were then $(l_2 - 2l_1)$ apart, and the number of Cd fringes corresponding to this length was obtainable by the method used in the first place for l_1 alone. This procedure was repeated throughout the etalon range, so that ultimately the longest etalon was determined in terms of the Cd wavelength.

Benoit, Fabry, and Pérot, and later workers used etalons of the normal Fabry–Pérot type, and observations on the Brewster fringes enabled consecutive etalons in the series to be compared. The longest etalons in these experiments were about 1 metre in length. Benoit, Fabry, and Pérot used five etalons in all; Sears and Barrell used only three, having lengths approximately 1, $\frac{1}{3}$, and $\frac{1}{9}$ metre. The latter workers used Brewster fringes formed by slight relative tilt of the etalons; Benoit, Fabry, and Pérot used parallel etalons and additional wedges to form these fringes (see p. 81).

(iii) In the last stage of each of these experiments the largest etalon was compared with the standard metre. Michelson's largest etalon was about 10 cm. in length, and the procedure at this stage was as follows. The longest etalon was placed alongside the standard metre and a fiducial mark on the etalon arranged in coincidence with one of the engraved limits of the metre, viewed under a high-power microscope. The etalon was moved backwards through its own length ten times, using the procedure already described for this operation. The fiducial mark on the etalon was then near the other engraved limit of the metre. Cadmium red fringes were counted during the additional movement of the etalon necessary to secure coincidence of the two engravings. The number of fringes so obtained corresponded to the small difference in length between the metre and ten times the largest etalon length.

In the other experiments the largest etalon was approximately a metre in length, and it was necessary to measure the small difference between its length and the true metre. If it were possible to lay the etalon and the standard metre side by side, and measure by microscope the distances between their length limits at each end, algebraic addition of these distances would give the required quantity. This is not possible, since the mirror edges under high magnification are not of the same sharpness and quality as the engravings * at the limits of the

---

* An engraving of the finest quality appears very broad under high magnification, and the centre of an ill-defined image must be chosen. An accuracy of $\pm \frac{\lambda}{2}$ in these settings corresponds to about one part in a million in the final determination.

metre. This difficulty was overcome in the Benoit, Fabry, and Pérot determination by engraving the end pieces of the etalon, which carried the two mirrors, with subsidiary high-quality engravings. These engravings defined a mechanical length of the etalon, a little different from its optical length. The difference between this mechanical length and the metre was found by the above-mentioned procedure; so that the only further requirement was a determination of the difference between the mechanical and optical lengths of the etalon. This is again essentially a length determination by optical means. The procedure was to use the same mirrors and end-pieces with two much shorter spacing pieces, such that the mechanical lengths were respectively about 1 and 2 cm. The optical lengths of both etalons were obtained by the method of exact fractions. Assuming that the two optical lengths so measured are l_1 and l_2, and x is the amount by which the mechanical length exceeds the optical length, the mechanical lengths L_1 and L_2 in the two cases are $(l_1 + x)$ and $(l_2 + x)$. A subsidiary plate with engravings P, Q, and R such that PQ and QR were both about 1 cm. was also employed. Microscope measurements gave the small differences k, m, and n between PQ and L_1, QR and L_1, PR and L_2. Thus, since $PR = PQ + QR$

$$(l_2 + x) + n = [(l_1 + x) + k] + [(l_1 + x) + m]$$

or,
$$x = (l_2 - 2l_1) + n - k - m$$

The required length x was determined in this way from the measurements.

Sears and Barrell's method was similar in principle to that of Benoit, Fabry, and Pérot, but included many refinements in technique, especially in the final stage of comparison with the standard metre. The refractive index of the air must be maintained uniform and constant by accurate temperature control in these experiments. Sears and Barrell held the temperature constant to $\frac{1}{1000}°$ C. The original accounts of the experiments may be consulted for further details (references 24–27).

It is evident that *end standards* (i.e., bars with polished plane ends, the distance between which is the standard length) are more suitable than line standards (bars with engravings), since the ends can be used directly in optical length tests, and the uncertainties associated with settings by microscope are avoided by their use. Techniques of construction now make it possible to produce end standards with greater accuracy than line standards. End gauges are used in workshop practice and may be measured, relative to a standard of the same type, with very high precision by these interferometric methods.

High-resolution spectroscopy by interferometric means

It has been observed previously in several connections that the resolving power obtainable with dispersive devices which depend on
interference principles is related to the number of interfering beams
and also the order of interference, increasing with both of these quantities.   With grating instruments it is necessary to be content with low
orders of interference, and the resolution is made as high as possible
by using many beams, i.e., many rulings on the grating.   Other devices
for producing high resolution (such as the Fabry–Pérot etalon and the
Lummer–Gehrcke plate) do so mainly by producing very high-order
interference effects, though the number of effective beams is also kept
as high as possible by the use of high reflecting surfaces upon the plates.
The highest resolution is obtainable with devices of the latter kind,
especially the Fabry–Pérot etalon, and only the very largest gratings
have resolution capabilities approaching those of any of these devices.
Gratings are discussed in Chapter 9; the present section briefly outlines spectroscopic techniques of the very-high-resolution type.   The
echelon grating, though similar in action in many ways to ordinary
gratings, uses high-order interference and a limited number of beams
and has high resolution capabilities, and is therefore most suitably
included in the present section.

The construction and action of the *Fabry–Pérot etalon* has already
been described.   When a parallel-sided etalon is employed and
parallel light is supplied over a wide range of incident directions, dispersion is produced in all directions perpendicular to the normal to the
etalon. Suppose now a narrow slit is placed in the focal plane of a lens
L_1 (see Fig. 8G (i)) and illuminated by monochromatic light, and the
light issuing from L_1 is allowed to fall on a Fabry–Pérot etalon F.P.
The directions of incidence upon the etalon are all nearly parallel to
one plane (the plane of Fig. 8G (i)), and therefore the emergent directions also all lie closely parallel to this plane.   If the issuing parallel
beams are focused by a further lens L_2 the effect in the focal plane
should be as shown in Fig. 8G (ii), only those portions of the system of
rings appearing which lie within the limits defined by the area S_2,
which is the image of S_1 formed by the system of lenses in the absence
of the etalon.   To tilt the etalon so that its normal does not correspond
to the axis of the lenses displaces the centre of the rings relative to the
area S_2; the centre of the rings will move along the length of S_2 if the
etalon normal remains in the plane of Fig. 8G (i).

When the light is composed of many wavelengths, rings of differing
radii appear in all the wavelengths, and if the fine structure of one
individual line is to be investigated the whole effect is too complex for
examination.   The procedure known as *crossed dispersion* is usually

employed to obviate this difficulty. The main wavelengths present in the source, any of which may be of complex hyperfine structure, are separated by the use of an auxiliary dispersive instrument, e.g., a prism.

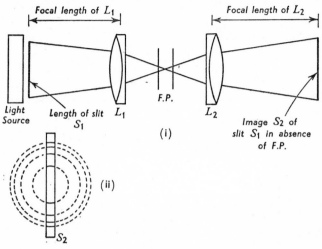

FIG. 8G.

Fig. 8H shows one way in which this may be done. The plane of this figure is such that the slit S_1 lies perpendicular to it. The images S_2', S_2'', etc., correspond to the main spectral lines, dispersed by the prism. Each of these is crossed by bright rings as shown in Fig. 8G (ii), since the etalon and the prism dispersions are at right angles. The hyperfine structure appears as a multiplicity of the ring systems within any line, and measurements upon these permit close estimations of the wavelengths and separations of the individual components. Other positions for the etalon relative to the spectrograph are possible; for some determinations it is more suitable to use it outside the slit S_1. Long etalons and long-focus high-quality camera lenses are required for the highest wavelength resolution.

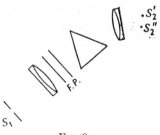

FIG. 8H.

The Lummer–Gehrcke plate is illustrated in Fig. 8J. This instrument consists of a plate of glass or quartz with parallel, optically flat surfaces, about 10–20 cm. long and a few millimetres thick. Light is internally reflected within the plate as shown, being made to enter the plate in the first place by the use of a small prism cemented to the end in either of the ways illustrated. The incidence angles within the plate are very near to the critical angle, so that the refracted light emerges in directions very close to the plate surface. Reinforcements occur for certain particular directions of the incident light so that the emergent light from either of the faces is concentrated in a number of parallel beams in well-defined directions, and these, when focused by a lens, produce sharp interference fringes, as illustrated in Fig. 8J (ii). The sharpness of the fringes arises because of the large number of interfering beams; multiple reflection takes place within the plate, since the condition that the incidence angle is just less than the critical angle is highly favourable to reflection. The fringes are essentially fringes of equal inclination, at very high angles to the surface normals. The fringes formed above and below the plate are identical; it is evident on con-

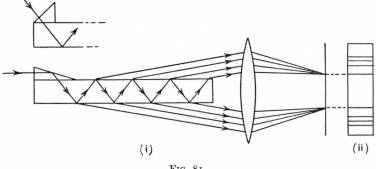

(i)   (ii)

FIG. 8J.

sideration that when the light is supplied within the plate, as it is effectively in this case, they would no longer be expected to be complementary as in other cases of reflected and transmitted fringes.

The instrument is normally used in such a way that its dispersion is crossed with that of a prism spectrograph. One arrangement is that of Fig. 8H with the Lummer plate replacing F.P., its thickness being parallel to the slit and its length in the light direction.

The limits to the plate thickness prevent the use of a Lummer–Gehrcke plate to obtain the highest resolutions, such as are possible with long Fabry–Pérot etalons. It is a useful and simple device, however, for a more limited range of applications. A quartz Lummer plate may be used in the ultra-violet region, where silvered surfaces have lower reflecting powers and therefore Fabry–Pérot etalons have much poorer resolution properties.

The *echelon grating* is another high-resolution device of importance. Echelons of both the transmission and reflection type were first conceived by Michelson (1898), and the former type was developed by him. Methods of construction of reflection echelons were first developed by Williams (1933). The transmission echelon is of relatively little importance, being inferior in many respects to other high-resolution instruments; but the reflection echelon is highly important, since it may be used over a very wide spectral range, from the infra-red to the far ultra-violet, and gives resolution which is inferior only to the Fabry–Pérot etalon used to its best advantage in this respect. Fig. 8K (i) and (ii) indicates the action of each of the types, Echelon gratings consist of a number of plates arranged in steps as indicated, the steps being equal in optical thickness in the transmission type, and equal in actual separation in the reflection instrument. Echelons are difficult

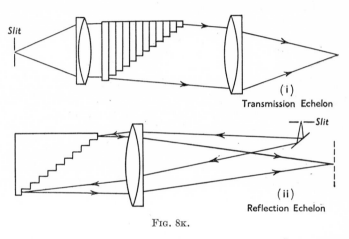

FIG. 8K.

and expensive to construct, and the upper limit to the number of steps is about 40. The steps are about 1 mm. across, transverse to the light direction, and about 1 cm. in depth, all the steps being identical in these respects. The effect is that of a coarse grating, but high-order interference of the diffracted beams takes place because of the optical-path differences introduced by the step depths. It is usual to cross the echelon dispersion with a prism-spectrograph dispersion, as with the other devices. For example, the arrangement of Fig. 8K (ii) may be external to a prism spectrograph, having its slit in the plane of focusing of the echelon spectra; the dotted line indicates the necessary direction of the spectrograph slit so that the dispersions may be crossed.

Air-films of different thicknesses between pairs of plates of a transmission echelon do not affect its action provided the plates are parallel. This is not so with the reflection echelon, so that definite closeness of fit between the individual plates is very important. Furthermore, the path difference between consecutive beams is $(n-1)t$ in the transmission type and $2t$ in the reflection type, and, since these quantities are in a ratio about 1:4, surface accuracies must be four times as good with reflection echelons as with the transmission type. The development of reflection echelons awaited the solution of these problems; Williams discovered it to be possible to obtain perfect optical contact of flats of fuzed quartz without pressure, the portions adhering very firmly. It is evident, however, that this type of instrument is very expensive because of the difficulties involved in its construction to the needed accuracy. The limitations imposed by the spectral range of transmission of the glass or other echelon material are not present with reflection echelons. Also, by silvering of the step faces, good intensities of the dispersed spectra are obtainable. One beam only is reflected at each step face, and the sharpness of the spectral lines is not dependent on the reflecting power as in the case of Fabry–Pérot interferometers, so that the resolving power does not fall off in the ultra-violet, where the reflecting properties of metal films deteriorate.

Fuller details of the use and relative merits of the instruments described in this section are available in reference 15.

The Twyman–Green interferometer

The Twyman–Green interferometer is similar in principle to the Fizeau interferometer described on p. 85. It is used for testing the shapes of wave-fronts transmitted by optical components such as prisms and lenses, and to indicate the way in which final local polishing of the surfaces of such components may bring the transmitted wave surfaces nearer to the ideal desired form. The instrument is illustrated in Fig. 8L (i), arranged for the testing of a prism. In construction it is in many respects similar to the Michelson interferometer, though there are important differences in its action. The source of light illuminates a very small circular aperture S at the focus of lens L_1 so that plane waves advance beyond L_1, being confined in direction to a very small angular range. These are divided into two sets of plane waves proceeding towards mirrors M_1 and M_2 as in the Michelson interferometer. Suppose first that the prism is of ideal form so that the plane waves remain plane on passage through it. Both sets of plane waves then retrace their paths by reflection at the high-quality mirrors M_1 and M_2, and about equal portions proceed in the direction of lens L_2 after leaving the surface Q again, and are converged by this lens to the aperture A at its focus. The eye is placed immediately behind A, so that it accepts the light arriving there in all directions from the lens L_2. The path difference between the beams is constant everywhere across their breadth, when both waves are plane and in exactly the same direc-

tion as they enter lens L_2. The eye therefore sees a uniform field
of illumination in these circumstances. Any imperfections in the
prism, either in its surfaces or in its homogeneity, will distort the wave-
front passing through it and result in differences of phase between the
two interfering beams, varying in amount across their breadth.
Fringes of equal optical thickness appear in the field viewed, which
represent the inequalities of path of the waves through the different
parts of the prism.   There is considerable depth of focus of the fringes,
because of the small range of directions of the light supplied, and it is
possible while viewing them to see also by reflection in Q a brush placed

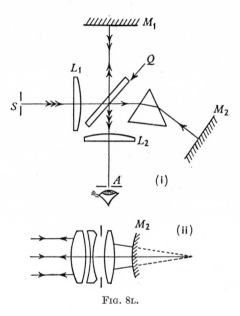

FIG. 8L.

in contact with one of the prism faces.   By means of this brush the
areas requiring polishing are marked out in wet rouge, and local polishing is then done with the prism removed, commencing at the centres
of these areas, where the optical thickness is too large, and working
outwards.   The progress of this local polishing can be observed by
viewing the fringes at any stage.

Fig. 8L (ii) shows as a further example how a lens may be tested
using a convex mirror M_2 to reverse the light direction.   The arrangement of Fig. 8L (ii) replaces the prism and plane mirror combination in
Fig. 8L (i).

Other instruments similar in kind to the Twyman–Green interferometer are in use.   Historically, the first instrument of this class was

the Mach–Zehnder interferometer (1891), which is a modification of the Jamin arrangement in much the same way as the Twyman–Green instrument is a development of Michelson's interferometer. Use of instruments of the Mach–Zehnder type has revived in recent years; one important application is in the aerodynamical field, where it may be used to examine pressure distributions in the air moving past aerofoils.

CHAPTER 9

INSTRUMENTAL APPLICATIONS OF INTERFERENCE AND DIFFRACTION

2. *GRATINGS*

An account of diffraction gratings may be conveniently divided into two main sections, on plane and concave gratings. The principles of action of the two types of grating are not essentially different; the concave grating provides its own focusing of the diffracted light, while this must be done by additional mirrors or lenses when plane gratings are employed. Methods of production of gratings, and effects depending on the quality and nature of their ruled surfaces, will first be indicated. This will be followed by an outline of the two main types of grating spectrometers, with some indication of their capabilities and uses.

Production and properties of gratings

High-precision grating ruling machines owe their development mainly to Rowland, during the period 1876–1901, though coarser gratings of moderate accuracy had been produced earlier by several investigators, after Fraunhofer had first shown the value of gratings in spectroscopic work. Rowland developed ruling engines to such an extent that his results have hardly been surpassed since. The accuracy required for the ruling of very fine gratings is such that even at the present time only a very limited number of workers possess the equipment and the ability for producing them. All ruling machines are similar in function; a succession of parallel grooves is scored on a surface which is advanced by means of a screw through a constant distance after each ruling. A diamond tool is used, and the surface is usually either of glass or metal. One of the major difficulties connected with this process is the inevitable introduction of periodic errors in the spacing of the rulings because of imperfections in the screw mechanism. These give rise to false spectra of various sorts, known as *ghosts*, and it is important in grating spectroscopy to anticipate the appearance of these ghosts in order not to be misled by them.

In the theoretical discussion of the action of a grating the rulings were considered as alternate opaque and clear strips of breadths b and a. It was shown how change in the relative magnitude of a and b affects the distribution of the light intensity over the various diffracted orders, though the directions of these orders remain the same provided that the grating element $(a + b)$ and the incident-light direction remain unchanged. More generally, any structure which repeats itself at regular intervals will act as a grating, producing intensity maxima in directions determined by the angle of incidence and the grating interval; the form of the grating element affects only the relative intensities in the orders. Some gratings, such as coarse wire gratings, and others ruled through thin metal deposits on glass so that the glass is exposed by the process of ruling, approximate to the alternate opaque and clear form. Most normal gratings do not do so, however, and the form of the grating element is determined by the depth and form of the grooves. The light distribution over the whole diffraction pattern is therefore very different from that obtained with a regular array of slits. The form of the grooves depends on the ruling point and the type of surface being ruled. Choice of a suitable diamond is therefore of great importance in the ruling of good gratings. It is possible in some cases to arrange the groove form in such a way as to concentrate most of the diffracted light into one order, thus minimizing one of the

Fig. 9A.

principal disadvantages of grating spectra, i.e., loss of intensity because the light is divided among several diffracted spectra. A good example of this is the *echelette grating*, introduced by R. W. Wood (1910). This is a reflection grating of the form illustrated in Fig. 9A, and is much used in the infra-red region, where relatively coarse gratings are adequate. For a certain angle of incidence the direction of reflection from the plane sloping faces of the individual rulings is also a direction of reinforcement, so that that particular diffraction maximum is aided by reflection, and therefore enhanced in intensity. Control over the shapes of the rulings is evidently easier for coarser gratings than for those with the finest spacings.

Rulings of about 15,000 lines/inch are frequently used for visual and ultra-violet spectral regions. Some ruling engines may be used to rule about 30,000 lines/inch. Coarser gratings are suitable for the infra-red region. Glass gratings are frequently used for transmission spectra. Speculum metal * has been often used for reflection gratings; it may be ground and polished, and is highly reflecting and reasonably resistant to corrosion. Aluminium (deposited on glass by evaporation and then

* An alloy containing about 70 per cent. Cu and 30 per cent. Sn.

ruled) has replaced speculum metal for many purposes in recent years. This is mainly because of its higher reflectivity, especially in the ultra-violet. Other metals have been used for special purposes. Glass is preferable to metal for reflection gratings using very high angles of incidence, since scattered light is less troublesome.

Replica gratings. It is evident from the foregoing account that successful grating ruling is an intricate and difficult process, and the output of good gratings is not large. Reproduction of the form of any ruled grating by obtaining a cast of its surface is clearly a process of possible value, and methods of achieving this have been known since 1905. Gratings produced in this way are known as replica gratings. A common method consists of covering the grating surface with a solution of pyroxyline in amyl acetate. After evaporation of the amyl acetate, the grating is immersed in water and the pyroxyline cast becomes detached from it, and is then mounted on a flat glass plate. There are several variations of this procedure. The replica gratings may be converted into reflection gratings by aluminizing, if this is desired. Replica gratings of this type are never so satisfactory as the original ruled gratings, but are suitable for a number of less-exacting purposes. This is mainly because of small thickness variations, arising during the drying process, which are difficult to eliminate.

Recently *Merton* has developed new methods of reproduction of gratings which are more satisfactory, and which may be used to form plane gratings from rulings made in the first place in the form of a helix on a cylindrical surface. He has described a procedure whereby such rulings may be made without introducing periodic errors; this consists in cutting a helix on one half of a metal cylinder and then copying it upon the other half in a way which corrects the periodic errors of the first. This technique, which, together with his method of replica production from these or other types of ruled surfaces, is of great promise for the production of very-high-quality gratings, and is being developed at the National Physical Laboratory, England.

The procedure for the production of the replicas is as follows. A cast of a grating surface in cellulose acetate is placed with the rulings down upon a wet gelatine layer on a flat glass plate. After drying and removal of the cast a positive copy of the rulings is obtained on the gelatine. A hard, durable surface is obtainable by using weak ammonium bichromate solution to soak the gelatine originally and by heat treatment of the replica when it has been formed. The surface so obtained may be washed without damage; it may also be aluminized if a reflection grating is desired. It may be used as an original from which more copies may be taken if desired. These replicas are much more satisfactory than the old type, since uniformity of thickness is much more easily obtained with gelatine. When the original rulings are on a cylindrical surface, this surface is first covered with cellulose acetate in a volatile solvent, and a wire placed on the ruled surface parallel to the cylinder axis makes it possible to divide the cylindrical cast when dry along this line, so that it may be straightened out ready for impression upon the flat gelatine surface.

Plane gratings

Except in the infra-red spectral region, mentioned below, there is considerably less preference for plane than for concave gratings in most serious spectroscopic work using gratings as the means of dispersion. This is mainly because the combination of diffraction and focusing properties of the concave type of grating makes the apparatus simpler, and little can be accomplished with plane gratings which is not possible with greater ease with the concave type. The infra-red region is at present the major field of application of plane gratings, spectroscopic investigations and technique in this region having developed rapidly in importance in recent years. Plane gratings have also been used in some special problems requiring high resolution. It will suffice to indicate briefly general arrangements of plane-grating spectrometers for the visual region, and to mention the modifications which are necessary in the infra-red.

The general arrangement of a plane-grating spectrometer is as follows. Radiation from an entrance slit illuminated by the source is collimated by one or more lenses or mirrors and allowed to fall on the grating. The diffracted parallel beams, which are transmitted or reflected according to the type of grating in use, are focused by lenses or mirrors to form the diffracted spectra. Most readers will be familiar with visual spectroscopes employing lenses and using a telescopic viewing system; this is the simplest form of the general arrangement. Alternatively, a camera lens with photographic material mounted in its focal surface, or some other means of detection moving across this surface (e.g., a photomultiplier tube), may be used for recording the spectra. The Littrow mounting, well known in prism spectroscopy, which uses the same lens for collimation of the light and focusing of the spectra, is shown in Fig. 9B as an example of a grating spectrograph. This mounting has been used with a 6-inch reflection grating and a very long focus lens (12 yards) in order to obtain highly resolved spectra. With the grating sufficiently tilted, diffracted orders up to about the 6th or 7th may be obtained (though they are weak) and a resolving power of about 5×10^5 is attainable. This is comparable, though still rather inferior, to that achieved with high-resolution interferometric devices such as the echelon grating and the Lummer plate.

In the infra-red, mirrors must replace lenses, since the latter are opaque, and the detectors may be of the thermopile, bolometer, or photosensitive types, depending on the region investigated. Coarser gratings are more suitable the more remote from the visible the wavelength region being studied, and even wire gratings are suitable further

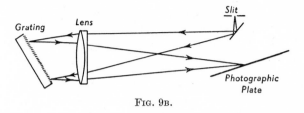

FIG. 9B.

into the long-wave region. The detector is usually fixed in position behind an exit-slit of the instrument and the spectrum scanned by rotation of the grating or one of the mirrors in the system.

Concave gratings

Rowland introduced the concave diffraction grating and developed much of the theory connected with it. Several of the possible mountings for concave gratings are based on the principle which is illustrated in Fig. 9c. If G is the pole of the concave ruled surface and C is its

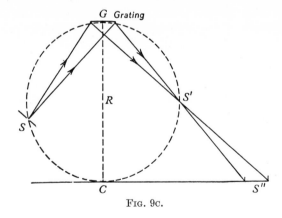

FIG. 9C.

centre of curvature, then the circle indicated in the figure, which has CG as its diameter, and has its plane perpendicular to the grating rulings, is known as the *Rowland circle*. If a short slit S has its centre anywhere on this circle, and is arranged parallel to the rulings, the combined effect of diffraction by the grating and astigmatic reflection at its surface is to produce a focused line image S', also with its centre on the

Rowland circle, its position depending on the wavelength and also on the order of diffraction. There is no point-to-point correspondence between the line image and the object slit; every point on the object slit produces a *line* at S', and these lines superpose, provided the slit length and the dimensions of the grating ruled surface are small compared with its radius. Actually the line image at S' corresponding to the point S on the Rowland circle is one of two astigmatic line images formed by the diffracted light of the wavelength concerned. The astigmatic reflected pencil is shown in Fig. 9C; the other line image is S''.

To record the diffracted spectra of any desired order it is evidently only necessary to mount photographic film so as to lie in the appropriate part of the Rowland circle. The various mountings of grating, object-slit, and photographic film, which make use of the above-mentioned principle, are now described in turn.

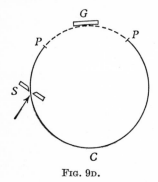

FIG. 9D.

The *Paschen mounting* applies the principle of the Rowland circle in the most general way. The slit S (Fig. 9D) is arranged to lie at some convenient general position on the Rowland circle, and in some cases may be adjusted in position upon it. Depending on the order of diffraction and the wavelength region to be studied, the photographic plate may be mounted anywhere upon the curved surface PP. Errors arising in the ruling of the grating often have the effect of shifting the surface of best focus slightly from the true Rowland surface. PP is therefore near to, but not quite coincident with, a considerable arc of the Rowland circle. Slight adjustment of the photographic plate mounting is made, and the best position is found by trial and error; this procedure is necessary also with other concave grating mountings.

The main characteristic of the Paschen mounting is the fixed relative position of slit, grating, and focal surface. Adjustment for different spectral regions is achieved simply by mounting the photographic material at different positions in the focal surface PP. The other concave grating mountings use a much more restricted portion of the Rowland circle for the recording of the spectra, and adjustment is achieved by relative movement of the components in such a way that they remain in position upon the Rowland circle.

The *Rowland* and *Abney* mountings may be mentioned together, since they are identical from an optical standpoint. In each of these the grating G and plateholder PP are fixed in relative position, being in

fact diametrically opposite upon the Rowland circle; the position of
the slit upon the Rowland circle is variable. This is done with the
Abney mounting by mounting the slit on a radius arm SB from the
centre B of the Rowland circle, as shown in Fig. 9E. In the Rowland
mounting (shown in Fig. 9F) the slit S is fixed in position, and the
grating G and plateholder PP are mounted at the ends of a rigid bar
GC, and move on guides which are at right angles and meet at S.
Two positions GC and $G'C'$ for the grating-camera unit are indicated
in Fig. 9F to show how the Rowland spectrograph is adjusted. The
Rowland and Abney mountings are mainly of historic interest. Almost
linear dispersion is obtained when the angles of reflection are near zero.
This is, however, no longer a very great advantage, since accurate
calibration of non-linear instruments is now possible using emission

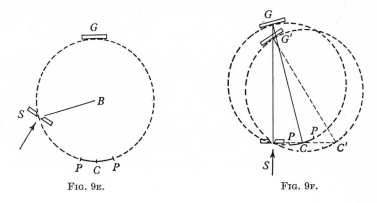

FIG. 9E.   FIG. 9F.

lines whose wavelengths are known with high precision by interferometric means. These mountings are inferior to others in most other
respects (e.g., soundness and accuracy of mechanical construction,
reduction of optical aberrations, compactness), and are therefore no
longer favoured.

The *Eagle mounting* (Fig. 9G) has the considerable advantage of
being very compact. The arrangement is similar to that of a Littrow
prism spectrograph, and the essential feature is that the diffraction
effects are observed over the same range of angles as the light is
supplied. By means of the small reflecting prism the light from the
slit S effectively originates at S' on the Rowland circle, and the diffracted
light is focused on the surface PP in the vicinity of S'. It is evident
that the arrangement is very economical in space, since it is confined
to a small volume along the direction $S'G$. Adjustment of these
instruments is rather complicated, however. The grating must be
moved along the line GS', and both the grating and plateholder must

be tilted appropriately (about axes perpendicular to Fig. 9G) in order to focus a new spectral region. Mechanical methods for effecting these adjustments have been evolved, which are rapid in operation but probably not so precise as careful systematic trial methods.

Two types of mounting may be mentioned which have been used in the extreme ultra-violet wavelength region. Investigations made in

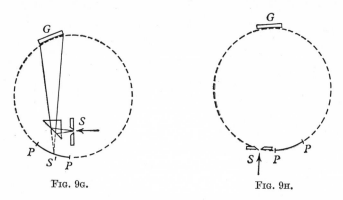

Fig. 9G.   Fig. 9H.

this region by Lyman, and by several later workers, have made use of the arrangement of Fig. 9H, the distinguishing feature of which is the use of incident and reflected directions, both of which are near to the normal to the grating. Evacuated spectrograph housings and special photographic emulsions (e.g., Schumann plates) are needed in this region.

The second arrangement, which has been used for the extreme ultra-violet and into the soft X-ray region as far as about 10 Å, is indicated

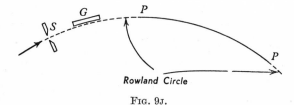

Fig. 9J.

n Fig. 9J. This is a development of the discovery made by Compton that a ruled grating could be used for the diffraction of soft X-rays provided nearly grazing incidence was used. Compton employed plane gratings and X-ray beams collimated by fine-slit arrangements. Osgood first used a concave grating and nearly grazing incidence as a means of investigating soft X-rays. The arrangement is evidently a special case of the Paschen mounting. Spectrographs of this type, even if employing long-radius gratings (up to 7 metres), may be housed within a small space, since slit, grating, and plateholder lie on a very small part of the whole Rowland circle circumference.

The *Wadsworth* or *stigmatic* mounting is mentioned last, since it is the only mounting employing a concave grating which does not make use of the principle of the Rowland circle. Here parallel light is incident upon the grating, and the diffracted beams near to the normal are usually investigated. Fig. 9K shows one arrangement. The combination of slit S and concave mirror M collimates the light. The parallel light falls upon the grating G, and is diffracted and focused into its focal surface PP, where the photographic material is mounted. The angle of incidence, and hence the wavelength region reflected to the plate, may be varied by swinging the arm GP relative to the remainder of the instrument. The use of the mirror for collimation improves the compactness of the arrangement and extends the spectral range which may be examined. Near the normal to the grating incident parallel beams focus to points after reflection, i.e., the reflected beams are stigmatic. In any wavelength there is thus point-for-point reproduction of the entrance slit S in the focal surface PP, and this mounting alone achieves this. The absence of astigmatism means that the intensity of the spectra is greater than with other mountings under similar conditions. It is also possible to use different sections of the slit length for producing several adjacent spectra for comparison purposes. With an astigmatic mounting this can be done only by having a movable aperture over the photographic plate itself. The dispersion is uniform with this mounting, since the plate is everywhere near the normal to the grating.

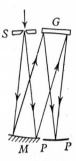

Fig. 9K.

References 12 and 13 may be consulted for fuller details upon the theory, adjustment, and relative merits of the various grating mountings. Numerical exercises on some grating mountings appear among the examples.

EXAMPLES

Assume the wavelength of maximum visual sensitivity (5500 Å) *where other wavelengths are not specified.*

1. A narrow slit is illuminated by sodium light of wavelength 5893 Å, and viewed from a distance through a further single slit held close to the eye and parallel to the first slit. Find the angular breadth of the central maximum in the diffraction pattern when the slit near the eye is 0·1 mm. broad. Indicate the effect of : (*a*) using white light; (*b*) broadening the illuminated slit.

2. Indicate the changes in the pattern seen when the illuminated slit of question 1 is viewed through a double slit held close to the eye. If the angular separation of the interference maxima obtained using sodium light is 8′, find the spacing of the double slit.

3. A biprism is mounted at a suitable distance from an illuminated slit, and biprism fringes are measured in a transverse plane 120·0 ± 0·2 cm. distant from the slit. Their mean spacing is 0·345 ± 0·005 mm. A thin lens is then arranged on the other side of the biprism from the slit, distant 23·0 ± 0·2 cm. from the slit. This lens forms two real images of the slit 5·72 ± 0·02 mm. apart in a plane 73·2 ± 0·3 cm. from the lens. Find the wavelength of the light used, and estimate the uncertainty in the result.

4. Newton's rings are produced using an optical flat and a spherical surface of large radius. Show that the square of the radius of the *m*th ring varies linearly with *m*. Find the gradient of the graph relating these quantities when the spherical surface has radius 100·0 cm. and light of wavelength 5893 Å is used.

5. Suggest, without detailed calculation, the form of the fringes of equal optical thickness produced when light is incident in near-normal directions upon thin films contained between the following pairs of surfaces : (*a*) a cylindrical surface lying upon an optical flat; (*b*) a cylindrical surface and an optical flat, the cylinder axis being not quite parallel to the flat surface; (*c*) an optical flat and a surface of " saddleback " shape (such as is obtained by bending a long flat glass plate).

6. Show that for equal-inclination fringes the order of interference decreases with increase of diameter of the rings; and that for an etalon of refractive index n and thickness e the order for the ring nearest the centre of the pattern is the largest integral number not greater than $2ne/\lambda$.

A parallel-sided thin air-film between silvered optical flats is illuminated by convergent light of wavelength 5893 Å. Consecutive equal-inclination fringes are observed at the following angles to the normal : 16° 16′, 19° 56′, 23° 05′, 25° 50′, 28° 21′, 30° 41′, 32° 52′, 34° 55′. Find the air-film thickness by plotting a suitable graph.

7. Find the order of the interference ring nearest the normal produced by a Fabry–Pérot etalon of optical thickness (*a*) 2 mm., (*b*) 10 cm., when light of wavelength 6000 Å is used. Find in each case the angular separation between (a) the 1st and 2nd rings, (b) the 10th and 11th rings, the rings being numbered from the centre outwards.

8. White light is incident on the slit of a spectroscope in a direction parallel to the collimator axis. An air-wedge with silvered glass surfaces covers the slit in such a way that its thickness varies uniformly from 2×10^{-3} mm. at one end of the slit to $2 \cdot 5 \times 10^{-3}$ mm. at the other. Calculate the positions of the main interference features appearing in the spectrum, and show these on a graph relating the vertical height within the spectrum with the wavelength.

9. A soap film of thickness 10,000 Å is illuminated normally by light which may be assumed equally intense at all wavelengths. Obtain an expression showing how the reflected-light intensity varies in the visible region with wavelength, and indicate graphically its form. As the film thickness becomes smaller, how will the form of this curve change?

10. A plane diffraction grating is illuminated normally by parallel light of wavelength 5890 Å. This light is deviated by an angle of 19° 22′ in the first-order spectrum. Find: (a) the grating interval; (b) the angle of dispersion between the wavelengths 7000 and 4000 Å in the second-order spectrum; (c) the new angle of incidence so that the second-order diffracted light of wavelength 5890 Å may be on the grating normal.

Plot graphs of deviation in the second-order spectrum against wavelength for the case of: (i) normal incidence; (ii) the angle of incidence found under (c).

11. A fine slit is arranged in the focal plane of a converging lens and illuminated by light of wavelength 6000 Å. The emergent light is focused by a second converging lens of focal length 30 cm. and on the same axis as the first. Three diffraction screens A, B, and C have respectively 1, 2, and 6 slits, all the slits being 0·1 mm. broad, and the opaque strips between the adjacent slits in screens B and C being all 0·3 mm. broad. Find how the intensity varies with distance off the axis in the focal plane of the second lens when each of these screens is placed separately between the two lenses (the screens are assumed to be inserted so that their slits are parallel to the illuminated slit, and the distances in the focal plane must be considered in a direction perpendicular to the slit lengths). On the same axes plot curves showing the intensity variations in the three cases.

12. A plane diffraction grating consisting of a very large number of alternate transparent and opaque lines, of breadths a and b respectively, is illuminated normally by parallel light of wavelength λ. Use the expression for the diffracted-light intensity distribution to confirm Babinet's theorem in this particular case, by showing that interchange of a and b does not alter the intensity in any direction other than along the grating normal. (Assume the number of lines in the grating $\rightarrow \infty$.)

13. The deflections of a galvanometer are measured by means of a lamp, filament, and scale. If the mirror attached to the galvanometer suspended system is circular and of diameter 5 mm., show that, because of diffraction at the mirror aperture, no great improvement in accuracy can be achieved by placing the scale more than about 4 metres from the mirror.

14. A small circular hole in an opaque screen is illuminated by sodium light (wavelength 5890 Å). It is viewed from a distance through a glass plate covered with a random distribution of fine circular obstacles of uniform diameter. Show that if the distance D cm. between the plate and screen is adjusted so that the first diffraction minimum around the hole is of a fixed diameter d cm., then the distance D is proportional to the diameter of the obstacles used. When the glass screen is lightly dusted with lycopodium powder $D = 102$ cm. when $d = 5\cdot0$ cm. Find the diameter of lycopodium particles.

15. Plot graphically the form of the transmission fringes produced by an air-spaced Fabry–Pérot etalon of thickness 0·01 mm., when the reflecting power (r^2) of the surfaces is : (i) 0·90; (ii) 0·60.

(Plot intensity against angular radius in the interference pattern, and use the wavelength $\lambda = 6000$ Å.)

16. In an experiment with a Michelson interferometer the light of the double sodium D line is used. The fringes alter in distinctness as the movable mirror is displaced steadily in one direction. The scale readings at two consecutive positions of minimum distinctness were found to be : (i) 69·39, 70·40, 68·40; (ii) 98·84, 98·05, 98·30. Taking the mean wavelength to be 5893 Å, calculate the difference in wavelength of the two components, and estimate the uncertainty of the result. The scale divisions are in hundredths of a turn of a screw of 1 mm. pitch.

17. On filling the evacuated tube of a Rayleigh interferometer with hydrogen to a pressure of 50 cm. of mercury it was observed that 145·7 fringes crossed the field of view. Assuming that $(n - 1)$ is proportional to density, calculate the refractive index of hydrogen at N.T.P. The length of the tube is 100 cm., the gas temperature 20° C, and the wavelength of the light 5893 Å.

18. Estimate the closest distance between two object points, at 25 cm. from the eye, which may be seen separately, assuming: (a) the normally accepted value of 1 minute for the resolving power of the eye; (b) that diffraction limits the detail viewable and the illumination conditions are such that the eye pupil diameter is : (i) 2·5 mm., (ii) 6 mm.

Account briefly in general terms for similarities and differences between the results obtained.

19. An astronomical telescope has a well-corrected objective of diameter 30 cm. and focal length 4·5 metres. Find : (a) the minimum power of the eyepiece if the optimum resolution in the image is to be obtained; (b) the resolving power of the instrument under the optimum conditions.

Assume the resolving power of the eye is 1·5 minutes of arc.

20. A lens of aperture $f/4$, which may be assumed aberration-free for distant objects, produces an image of an axial object point at infinity. Find the diameter of the central intensity maximum in the diffraction pattern produced. Using the Rayleigh limit, find the longitudinal range of adjustment of the image-plane position within which the optimum focus of the image would be obtained. Explain why, over a considerably larger longitudinal range of image plane positions, no deterioration in focus of the image would be visible to the eye without enlargement of the image.

21. Find the resolving power of Fabry–Pérot etalons of spacings 5 mm. and 10 cm. when the reflecting power of the surfaces is : (a) 0·90; (b) 0·70.

22. For each of two lines of wavelengths 6000·0 and 6000·1 Å calculate the highest order of interference produced by a Fabry–Pérot etalon of spacing 5 mm. Find the diameters of the corresponding fringes formed in the focal plane of a lens of focal length 20 cm. Find also the diameters of the next three fringes of lower order in each of the wavelengths. Indicate on a diagram the appearance of the double-fringe system.

23. A beam of light falls normally on a reflection echelon which has N steps having dimensions p cm. in the light direction and q cm. transverse to the light direction. Show that the path difference between light beams diffracted in the direction θ with the normal, from corresponding points on consecutive step faces, is

$$p(1 + \cos \theta) - q \sin \theta$$

Hence show that, when θ is small, the condition for the mth order interference maximum is

$$m\lambda = 2p - q\theta$$

If $p = 1$ cm. and $q = 0·1$ cm., find, for light of wavelength 5000 Å, the magnitudes of the orders reflected near to the normal, and the angular separation between consecutive orders. Assuming that the resolving power is given by mN, as with a simple grating, find the minimum resolvable wavelength difference when $N = 40$.

24. Obtain expressions applicable to a transmission echelon grating, similar to those obtained in Question 23 for a reflection echelon, using n to indicate the refractive index of the echelon material. Assuming $n = 1·5$ and the other dimensions as given in Question 23, find, in the transmission case, the quantities asked for in Question 23.

25. Show that the general formula for the direction of the mth-order diffraction maximum produced by a reflection grating is

$$(\sin i + \sin i') = Mm\lambda$$

where M is the number of rulings per cm. of the grating breadth, and i and i' are the angles made by the incident and the diffracted light with the normal, these angles being given opposite signs when they are on opposite sides of the normal.

26. A concave grating of radius R cm. has M rulings/cm. A slit is mounted on the Rowland circle so that the light passing through it falls on the grating at an angle of incidence i. The mth order diffracted light of wavelength λ focuses on the Rowland circle at a distance l cm. around its circumference from the pole of the grating, and i' is the angle to the normal at which this light leaves the grating. Show that $l = R\left(\dfrac{\pi}{2} - i\right)$ and

$$\frac{dl}{d\lambda} = \frac{MmR}{\cos i'} \times 10^{-8} \text{ cm./Å}$$

27. Using the equations proved in Questions 25 and 26 and assuming that $i = 45°$, $M = 5000/\text{cm.}$, and $R = 5$ metres, find :

(*a*) the range of values of l covered by the visible spectrum (4000–7500 Å) in the first and second orders.

(*b*) the wavelengths diffracted in the normal direction and the linear dispersions at near-normal directions in the first- and second-order spectra.

BIBLIOGRAPHY

This list of references is by no means exhaustive, but is intended to give the reader guidance in the first stages of more advanced reading on the subject. A few particular papers, referred to in the text because of their interest in various connections, are also listed here.

Books

1. BRUHAT, G. (1947). *Optique.* Masson, Paris.
2. CANDLER, A. C. (1951). *Modern Interferometers.* Hilger and Watts, London.
3. CONRADY, A. E. (1929). *Applied Optics and Optical Design,* Part I. Oxford.
4. COULSON, C. A. (1952). *Waves.* Oliver and Boyd.
5. DITCHBURN, R. W. (1952). *Light.* Blackie.
6. DRUDE, P. (1902). *Theory of Optics.* Longmans.
7. GLAZEBROOK, R. (1923). *Dictionary of Applied Physics,* Vol. 4. Macmillan.
8. HEAVENS, O. S. (1955). *Optical Properties of Thin Solid Films.* Butterworths.
9. HOPKINS, H. H. (1950). *Wave Theory of Aberrations.* Oxford.
10. JAMES, R. W. (1948). *The Optical Principles of the Diffraction of X-rays.* Bell.
11. MARTIN, L. C. (1948 and 1950). *Technical Optics,* 2 volumes. Pitman.
12. MEYER, C. F. (1934). *Diffraction of Light, X-rays, and Material Particles.* University of Chicago Press.
13. SAWYER, R. A. (1945). *Experimental Spectroscopy.* Chapman and Hall.
14. TOLANSKY, S. (1948). *Multiple Beam Interferometry of Surfaces and Films.* Oxford.
15. — (1947). *High Resolution Spectroscopy.* Methuen.
16. WILLIAMS, W. E. (1950). *Applications of Interferometry.* Methuen.
17. WOOD, R. W. (1947). *Physical Optics.* Macmillan.

Review Articles

18. BOUWKAMP, C. J. (1954). Diffraction Theory. *Reports on Progress in Physics,* Physical Society, London, **17**, 35.
19. KUHN, H. (1951). New Techniques of Optical Interferometry, *ibid.,* **14**, 64.
20. WOLF, E. (1951). Diffraction Theory of Aberrations, *ibid.,* **14**, 95.

Papers

21. CHILDS, W. H. J. (1926). *Jour. Sci. Inst.,* **3**, 97 and 129.
22. GOUY, A. (1891). *Ann. de Chimie et de Physique.,* Ser. *VI,* **24**, 145.

23. NICOLSON, M. M. (1954). *Proc. Leeds Phil. and Lit. Soc., Scientific Section*, **6**, 119.
24. MICHELSON, A. A., and BENOIT, J. R. (1895). *Trav. et Mem. Bur. Int. des Poids et Mesures, Vol. II.*
25. BENOIT, J. R., FABRY, C., and PÉROT, A. (1913). *Ibid.*, Vol. 15.
26. SEARS, J. E., and BARRELL, H. (1932). *Phil. Trans. Roy. Soc.*, **231**, 75.
27. — (1934). *Ibid.*, **233**, 143.
28. ROGERS, G. L. (1954). *Am. Jour. Phys.*, **22**, 384.

RECENT BOOKS (*added in proof*)

29. TOLANSKY, S. (1955). *An Introduction to Interferometry.* Longmans.
30. FLÜGGE, S. (1956). *Encyclopedia of Physics*, Vol. 24. *Fundamentals of Optics.* Berlin. Springer–Verlag.

INDEX